By the same author

PLANTED TREES

GREEN GLORY

The Story of the Forests of the World

WORLD'S WONDER TREES.

GREEN GLORY

The Story of the Forests of the World

by

RICHARD ST. BARBE BAKER

With a Foreword by

HOWARD SPRING

LUTTERWORTH PRESS
LONDON and REDHILL

*This book is produced in
complete conformity with the
authorized economy standard*

*Printed in Great Britain by
The Camelot Press Ltd., London and Southampton*

ACKNOWLEDGMENTS

T O SO MANY PEOPLE I OWE A DEBT OF GRATITUDE FOR THE helpful way in which they have assisted me in my life-long study of trees and forestry. But for their help I could not have attempted this present work. It was my father who first initiated me into the art of growing trees. As a small boy he allowed me to work with him in his nurseries in the village of Westend in Hampshire. It is impossible to make acknowledgments to my many teachers whose words of wisdom guided me in my studies in many lands.

More than a formal acknowledgment is due to the diplomatic representatives of the forty-four nations who for the past few years have been co-operating with me, and who have provided information about the forests of their countries. In the course of my travels I have enjoyed the kindness and hospitality of numerous foresters, who have accompanied me to their forests and have opened their hearts about their particular problems of conservation.

To mention all the books that I have consulted would entail listing most of the works on my shelves, but among those that have been especially helpful are: *The Trees of Great Britain and Ireland*, by John Henry Elwes and Augustin Henry; *Timbers of Commerce* and *Textbook of Wood*, by Herbert Stone, Professor in Wood Technology, Cambridge; *Plants*, by Sir Albert Seward, Professor of Botany, Cambridge, under both of whom I studied at Cambridge; *Aims and Methods in the Study of Vegetation*, by A. G. Tansley, F.R.S., and Dr. T. F. Chipp; *History of Forestry*, by Dr. Fernow, Dean of the Faculty of Forestry, University of Toronto; *The Land Now and To-morrow*, by Sir George Stapledon; *Alternative to Death*, by the Earl of Portsmouth; *The Rape of the Earth*, a masterly survey of soil erosion by G. V. Jacks and R. O. Whyte; *Humus and the Farmer*, by Friend Sykes, the last four being published by Faber and Faber, who have sponsored so many valuable books dealing with the land. To *The Empire Forestry Handbook 1946* I owe many valuable statistics, and my thanks are due to Major P. M. Synge, for his descriptions in *Borneo Jungle* (Lindsay Drummond); to V. A. Firsoff for *The*

Tatra Mountains (Lindsay Drummond), and to Dr. George Borodin for an extract from *Soviet and Tsarist Siberia* (Rich and Cowan). Other books I have consulted are *The U.S.S.R. A Geographical Survey*, James S. Gregory and D. W. Shave (George G. Harrap & Co., Ltd.); *Extinct Plants and Problems of Evolution*, Dr. D. H. Scott (Macmillan & Co.); *Sagas of the Evergreens*, Frank H. Lamb (The Bodley Head); *Green Mountains*, Bernard O'Reilly (W. R. Smith and Patterson Pty., Ltd.); *Big Trees*, Walter Fry and John R. White (Stamford University Press); *Earth's Green Mantle*, Professor Sydney Maughan (The English Universities Press); *The Nation's Forests*, William Atherton Du Puy (The Macmillan Company); *The Structure and Life of Forest Trees*, by Dr. Bügen, translated by Thomas Thomson, M.Sc. (Chapman and Hall Ltd.); *The Poems of Henry Van Dyke* (Charles Scribner's Sons); and the new edition of *Chambers's Encyclopædia*. To Dr. Ovid Butler I am indebted for help from his journal, *American Forests*, and to many friends and members of the Society of American Foresters and to their *Journal of Forestry*. Grateful acknowledgment is due to Dr. Franz Heske, author of *German Forestry*, who very kindly accompanied me with a party of forestry students from Oxford on a tour in Eastern Germany, Austria, and Czechoslovakia.

To many of those mentioned in the bibliography I owe a debt for the contact of personal friendship as well as the written word. The assistance of Mr. Henry G. Finlayson, Executive Secretary of The Men of the Trees, has been invaluable, and I would like to thank Miss Sylvia Kershaw and members of Headquarters Staff, especially Miss Ann Gilbert, for typing and taking down rough drafts, and Miss Naish for preparing a fair copy of the manuscript.

Throughout all I have had the inestimable help and support of my wife, whose constant care during my convalescence enabled me to complete *Green Glory*.

CONTENTS

LIST OF ILLUSTRATIONS

Photographs by the Author except where otherwise stated

FOREWORD

MR. RICHARD ST. BARBE BAKER, WHO KNOWS THE FORESTS of the world as intimately as most of us know the privet hedges in our own back gardens, and who knows individual trees like the great redwoods as familiarly as we know our favourite dogs, has put his unique experience of these matters into a number of books. If I were asked to say in a sentence what it is that he seeks to teach us through these books, I should answer shortly: "All flesh is grass."

This famous saying is too often accepted as meaning only that the life of man is brief. He "to-day is, and to-morrow is cast into the oven". But there is more to it than that. Every moment that he draws breath here below man is dependent on the grass of the field for his very being. Sir Thomas Browne knew this and pointed it out in *Religio Medici: "All flesh is grass* is not only metaphorically but literally true; for all those creatures that we behold are but the herbs of the field digested into flesh in them, or more remotely carnified in ourselves." In the fourth chapter of this present book, Mr. Baker puts the same thought into a few words: "Thus the tree, with the help of all plant life, controls the food supply and life of man and of the animal kingdom."

If I had been writing that myself, I should have said: "Thus the tree, with the help of all plant life, controls the food supply of the animal kingdom, and man will forget at his peril that he is a member of that kingdom."

A great deal of Mr. Baker's writing in all his books—and the present book is no exception—has been concerned with the disasters that follow when man forgets that he is not the world's master, but one of many tenants. The tenants are animate and inanimate—or so we chose to call them, though the animation of a tree is an inescapable thing, and some trees take on the proportions of majestic personality. But, call them what we may, the farther we go into the matter the more deeply we apprehend that men and trees, grass and birds, the beasts of the field and all living things, are held in a balance that may not lightly be disturbed. Even that which seems meanest is a note in what should be a harmony and is too often a discord; which is the inner meaning of that strange saying that not even a sparrow shall fall to the ground "without your Father".

Not till this is far more deeply understood than it is to-day will man approach that condition of prosperity which he now all too often imagines can be reached by "gadgets". Fall in with the ways of Nature and prosper; fall out with them and disaster is inevitable. Not that "falling in" means acquiescence with all that Nature wants to do. No farm, for instance, is "Nature" as it would be if left to its own devices. The point is that Nature must be coaxed and wooed, not ravished; its ways of going to work must be understood and sympathized with if we are to attain the ends which are both ours and hers. And in the long run there must always be a sense in which man, in relation to Nature, is both slave and master. But this is too wide a subject to be gone into here.

We find in this book some truly terrifying pictures of man flying in the face of Nature, ruthlessly uprooting and burning the very stuff that holds the world together; and no less terrible pictures of Nature making her implacable reply. Man strips the forests of China; Nature swirls away in the Yellow River every year 2,500,000 tons of the soil on which man might live. Man strips the western prairies to the bone; Nature hands him a dust-bowl. So the folly and the retribution go on, and have gone on throughout the centuries as civilizations have risen and decayed.

Can the process be stopped? Will man learn to work with Nature, realizing, as Mr. Baker so well puts it, that the bounty of Nature is not his to squander, but is an "entail" for the good of all generations? Well, much has been done; how much this book will tell you; and you will learn here, too, how much our author has himself contributed to the redemptive work, with what energy and knowledge he has ranged the whole world, seeking to stem the tide of destruction. He poses the problem in its forbidding magnitude, and reaches the conclusion that only concerted action by every country can repair a situation that has tended for so long to get out of hand. He would for one thing—and this seems to me a splendid idea—turn all the standing armies of the world on to forestry work. Goodness knows, the armies have eaten our green life like locusts; it would be only reasonable if they repaired their own ravages.

Would the nations, which seem so fatally disinclined to collaborate upon anything, collaborate upon this? Could they be persuaded that the life of trees matters? They could, if it were once sufficiently known that men and trees live or die together. Here is a small instance with a large significance. To the north of the Gold Coast, Mr. Baker tells us, the destruction of the forest has let in the desert, which is advancing rapidly. The people are being driven into a narrowing strip of trees. "Here may be witnessed racial suicide on a bigger scale than the world has ever before seen. Knowing the end of the forest to be near, and with little chance of getting food, the chiefs have forbidden marriage, and the women refuse to bear children, for they will not raise sons and daughters for starvation."

When improvidence goes so far that one edition of an American newspaper consumes twenty-four acres of forest, it is not difficult to imagine a too-near time when the plight of those Negroes shall be the plight of millions of mankind. Only knowledge, implementing a rational co-operation with Nature, can avert such a disaster; and I am not aware of any writer to-day who spreads that knowledge more fruitfully than Mr. St. Barbe Baker.

HOWARD SPRING.

GREEN GLORY

When God, all glory, fashioned—
Flashed the first bright light
From Heart of hearts,—impassioned
Life of Life, delight
He knew in Nature's green
That ran the Earth around,
A verdant spirit, clean
And pure upon the ground.
Thus waked the soul of Earth
Into a perfect tree,
And all the forest birth
From it, was come to be.
Onward green glory shone
At peace with rhythmic swing,
As leaf with leaf, upon
The trees did timely spring.
Then as the scale did fall—
O'er burdened with green light,
In summer, over all—
Bare branches came in sight
With gesture to up-hold
The sap-returning scale
Of life, that winter cold
Could never long assail.
And so the flame ran on,
With benediction peace;
Thus quiet beauty shone
Green fire, without cease:
And God saw it was good.
Then fashioned He mankind
Whose seed misunderstood
With self-asserting mind,
The glory of the tree,
And with a ruthless hand
Curtailed fertility
Upon the fruitful land.
The flame of glory waned,
And drought and dreary dearth
Laid waste the woods, and planed
The lovely curves of Earth,
Whose soul was gone from sight.
Then man repented him
And strove to kindle light
Where he had made Earth dim.

．　　．　　．　　．　　．

Man now plants many trees
To glorify their birth,
Since God intended these
Should shine from heart of Earth.

Written for *Green Glory* by Catherine Blakiston.

Chapter One

COSMORAMA

*In the beginning God created the heaven and the earth . . .
and saw that it was good.*

Gen.: I.

IMAGINE YOU ARE HIGH UP IN THE STRATOSPHERE, GLIDING
on a magic carpet, transparent, so that you can look
down without anything to obstruct your view. Imagine
that you are slowly approaching our planet in line with the
North Pole, and that you are hovering sufficiently far away to
view in perspective the Polar regions. It is summer. You have
perfect visibility and telescopic vision and you are looking
down on the Arctic ice glistening white and hummocky, the
Paleocrystic Sea. The ice is in constant motion. The great land
mass that forces itself on your view is Greenland, a continent
in itself. You will pick up Iceland and Spitzbergen. Between
these lands great masses of hummocky ice are for ever moving,
blocking the waters, piling up and cracking asunder, constant
movement in all directions.

If you were to dive on your magic carpet and hover a few
hundred feet over this moving mass, you might see whole pine
trees frozen in the ice. Whence did they come? For no living
vegetation is in sight. What magic forces brought them into
this maelstrom of ice? Were they carried right across the Pole
from the rivers of the old and new worlds? From your point
of vantage you may retrace their journeyings back to the
virgin forests from which they were torn.

Let your magic carpet take you back into the stratosphere,
so that you may continue your Arctic exploration. Beyond
the masses of hummocky ice you will be able to scan a narrow
band of open land, which runs at great length and varying
widths. This is the open, brown tundra, with vast swampy
plains which border on the Arctic Ocean. They are the Arctic
deserts. If you had to live there you would find the climate
terrible, the cold intense, and the soil frozen to a great depth,

B

for it only thaws on the surface during the short summer. In the tundra plants do not reach tree height, though a few of the most hardy species survive as low bushes, rising but a few inches above the ground. Where trees are not, in the most unfavourable conditions may be found lichens, mosses, reeds, and brightly flowering bulbs of many colours. Where conditions are less severe, small berry-bearing shrubs and those with catkins may be seen, cranberries too, and tiny willows.

Within the Arctic Circle, beyond the tundra, you will see a great dark green mantle stretching on and on, almost unbroken. The transition from tundra to the coniferous forest which lies to the south is very gradual. First single trees appear, then groups in irregular formation, and finally the tundra is dotted with thousands of small forests. These are the evergreen forests of the cone-bearing trees, sometimes known as softwoods, although in fact many of them are quite hard, for, having grown slowly in the cold, such trees are noted for their toughness. Throughout the whole of this region, growth is restricted by a long cold period; yet the forest itself tends to modify the climate, reducing the speed of winds and raising the temperature. The surface soil is thawed in summer. Protected by the foliage, deep snow, and the forest floor of decaying humus, the earth does not freeze to any great depth even in winter, and so it is possible for deep-rooted trees to grow and flourish.

You will feel the monotony of uniformity in this great green belt which stretches almost unbroken but for clearings here and there for farms. On it goes from Norway, through Finland, the Russias, and Siberia. Here the forests extend to the south of 56° north, covering the slopes of the Altai and Sayan Mountains, and march in the highland regions of Transbaikalia and the Amur Basin. Even at a great height you can observe that the chief trees of Western Siberia are fir, cedar, spruce, stone pine, and Siberian larch. The Urami, a mixture of marsh and forest, covers large areas. As you pass over South-western Siberia, fir and cedar dominate, while birch and aspen cover large areas and may be seen with alder, willow, and mountain ash in thickets. As you proceed into Eastern Siberia the larch forest extends, and in Transbaikalia

"On it goes"—flying over the Chechem Gorge in Kabarda, U.S.S.R.

"These are but isolated outposts"—the Himalayas near Dharmasala, Kangra Valley.

you see pine forests in the deeper valleys. Over all hangs a gloom unbroken by the notes of song birds. Only in South-western Siberia the birch and aspen vary the scene, while in the more open spaces tall rich grass and ferns, with occasional clumps of juniper, bring welcome relief to the monotony of the dark conifers.

On then into Manchuria and Korea, where you will see new forests taking the place of this more cheerful vegetation. From your high point of vision you will have seen that the evergreen forest encloses the flanks of the Alps, with detached areas in the lands bordering the Mediterranean. In Western Russia you will have observed that it joins up with the broad-leaved forests, and farther east is held up by the Steppes. In part of Asia the southern boundaries fade into deserts and the grass-lands of Turkestan, of Mongolia, and of Manchuria. Around the mighty mountains of Tibet the green of the conifers is present and appears in the Himalayas, though these are but isolated outposts in comparison with the great belt of evergreen which runs ever eastward in Siberia, extending from the Arctic belt.

Crossing the Bering Sea, you will pick up a tiny spot of evergreen on the island of St. Lawrence, a link in the land bridge which once connected Asia with Alaska. That white ribbon curling over the mountains and winding through the forests is road, the new link from the East with this once remote part of the continent. Along the Alaskan Peninsula and within the coast range are the magnificent cedar forests interspersed with Douglas and Sitka. In North America you will see that the coniferous belt becomes streaky and is enlivened with birches and maples with their glorious autumn colouring, a relief from the oppressive monotony of the Siberian forests.

As your magic carpet glides eastwards, you will recognize four distinct regions: that of the Rockies, with its tree-clad slopes, lakes, and mountain torrents; the prairies of the Middle-west, ground hilly, undulating, or flat, with bluffs of poplar dotted here and there; the Great Lakes regions around Superior, with their vast forests of spruce and pine—pine covering the Thirty Thousand Islands of the Georgian Bay; finally, the forest region of Quebec, with its front door along the St. Lawrence, gateway to the East.

As you travel south you follow the trail of forest destruction, but here and there are the remains of what must have been majestic forests, and abandoned farms are once again being taken in by the trees, showing that Nature heals her scars. As you fly above the great State of New York, you pass over the nurseries of Syracuse which are providing millions of trees for the reclamation of the marginal lands. You pass over the northern hardwood regions, the maple, beech, and yellow birch, and down through the Carolinas into Florida, with its swamp-cedar and pitch-pine. Missing the Gulf of Mexico, you cross the islands of Cuba and Jamaica and find yourself gliding down the dense green tropic zone which connects the Northern and Southern Americas. This is unbroken evergreen tropical forest. Greater variety presents itself as you fly over the huge territory of Colombia. The northern zone is hilly and dry, and in summer, or the dry season, many of the great trees are leafless. Here are the great macondos and the bombacopsis occupying the drier gravelly areas in the region of plentiful rainfall.

Next comes British Guiana with its greenheart forests, and before you know where you are the magic carpet takes you across the Amazon and its great tributaries, draining the greatest tropical forests of the world. The sombre sameness of the evergreen bush is brightened by the reflected light of the sun on its glistening leaves. This is a region of mystery, and from the air it all looks alike dazzlingly lovely, with bright-plumaged birds in the tree tops, with flowers in profusion and subtle scents.

Trailing down into the heart of Brazil, you see broad belts of evergreen, and as you continue your journey south you fly for a thousand miles along a coastal belt of equatorial and tropical forests. The coast of this delectable land is swept by the warm current which bears the name of the country. From the stratosphere, Paraguay and Uraguay blend imperceptibly into Brazil and the Argentine. The vegetation thins out as the rainfall decreases, and becomes more stunted and diminishes, until in Patagonia trees take on pygmæan forms. You must now cross the pampas to the Pacific coast to pick up the green belt once more. A mere glance will show the great

"The Great Lakes regions with their vast forests of spruce and pine"—Northern Ontario.

"India with its monsoon forests"—looking down on Darjeeling.

inroads now being made into the main timber forests of the coastal range.

As you hover over the South Pole, you will see little more than great mountains of ice, a vast inhospitable region with an ice cap surrounded by the Antarctic Sea; covering more than half of your visible world, the only unfrozen land projecting into it being the point of South America. As the Continent of Australia comes into your vision, you will find that this great land mass presents desert conditions, except for the narrow fringe of sub-tropical evergreen surrounding the coast. As you survey New Zealand, you will see open farmlands and sheep-runs where unbroken vistas of native trees once reigned, but once again the pumice lands of the North Island are being clad with many exotic species, including the Monterey pine from California.

Proceeding north-west, you will traverse the rich forests of New Guinea, Borneo, the Philippine Islands, Java, and Sumatra. Taken as a whole, the forest wealth still remains intact in this area, and with the introduction of systematic management will make a valuable contribution to the reconstruction of the Far East. Great are the trees of the Malay Peninsula which vie with each other in their tropical luxuriance. The Indo-China Peninsula presents a great variety of scene, ranging from tropical forest to sub-tropical evergreen woodlands. Teak is the dominant species of Burma, and as you cross the Irrawaddy you will see great rafts of this valuable species being floated downstream to the port of Rangoon, while up in the forest elephants are hauling the huge logs along forest trails and pushing them into swift-travelling currents which bear them on their way to the great river. India, with its monsoon forests, has a greater variety of species than any other sub-tropical or temperate zone, but the hill-cultivators have stripped the virgin forest from many a mountainside and over vast areas gully and sheet erosion is catastrophic.

Although China claims nearly 300 million acres of forest, long utilization has ruined the land around the head waters of the Yellow River until it has become the worst eroded region in the world. As your magic carpet lingers over Japan, with its steep valleys covered with loose volcanic soils, you will see that, wherever the vegetation cover is broken on the slopes, immediate disaster is threatened; but vegetation has been quickly restored, for the Japanese, with their coniferous and broad-leaved forests, have learnt how to control the threat of erosion.

As you once again steer westwards and cross the Yellow Sea, you follow the Yellow River, so aptly named, for it is coloured with a yellow subsoil that still pours into it from the now barren loessial hinterland. For hundreds of miles along its course you will see that the bed of the Yellow River is raised higher and higher above the surrounding country by the continual deposition of eroded soil which has torn down the hillsides in increasing torrents in the most disastrous floods the world has seen. As you follow the trail of ancient migrations and vanished civilizations, you will see little but desolation. It will be difficult to adjust your eyes to the vastness of the untreed desert, or your senses to the austerity of silence and solitude of the tedious wastes of Gobi and Lob. However breathless the day, you will be sure to see a slender spiral of sand rising. It will move, circle, walk across the plain, leave the earth, and vanish in the sky. At times the whole desert floor is alive with them. From your high altitude they may seem insignificant, but to the wanderer in the wilderness they are fearful in their cyclonic force. They are what the travellers call dust-spouts, but the desert-dweller calls them dust-demons. Like ghostly beings, they wrap their garments of dust about them and whirl from left to right or right to left—"Male and female," say the men of the desert: "you can distinguish them by the way they fold their cloaks around them, right to left or left to right, see how they come in pairs."

Passing westward over the sandy deserts of Turkestan, it is hard to realize that they have ever provided pasture for the Astrakhan sheep and camels. Great were the flocks of ancient times in south-eastern Karakum, which formerly supplied Bokhara with hides to the value of millions of roubles. Now the advancing dunes, no longer bound by vegetation, threaten the populations in the oases and narrow river valleys, and each year bury large areas of highly fertile, irrigated land. As you skirt the southernmost point of the Caspian Sea, you will observe that it is fringed with evergreen trees and shrubs, while south lie the great plateaux of Iran, once covered with the green glory of the forests. This was the cradle of civilization, and as generations grew and flourished, making ever greater demands on the forest land, whole populations passed their prime and became exhausted by the slow wastage that accompanies the processes of natural growth and decay.

Dive over the southern side of Anatolia and see how the ancient ports are now silted up: Tarsus, visited by Cleopatra's fleet, is now an inland town ten miles from the sea, while the mouth of the Great Menderez River has advanced seawards through upland erosion. You will fly over countries rich with fruit-bearing trees, for this is the garden of the Mediterranean. The coniferous forest dominates the northern parts of the Balkans, while evergreens emerge in the coastal ranges. Although you would like to linger on your magic carpet over Southern Europe, with its vineyards and citrus groves, you have yet to visit Arabia and span the Continent of Africa. It is hard to imagine that Arabia was once wooded, that Palestine was a land flowing with milk and honey, or that the wilderness of Sinai had manna-bearing trees to feed the old-time wanderers from Egypt. Scan the continent of Africa in perspective and see how little forest remains. Down the east coast by comparison there is the merest fringe.

Glide over Madagascar and, but for the east coast, little forest growth is present. Along the central equatorial coastal regions of East Africa are the mangrove swamps, extending for hundreds of miles along a thousand miles of water-front. These swamp forests thrive between high and low water, throwing out their aerial roots, which fix them along the muddy creeks. The coastal tropical forest is narrow, mixed evergreen and deciduous, and this borders on the Nika, or desert country, which stretches west for many hundreds of miles. In the mountain regions of Kenya, Kilimanjaro and the Aberdares are the coniferous and broad-leaved zones which fringe the bamboo forests, giant grasses towering sixty feet in height. Dropping down to the great lakes, the forest is left behind and sud and papyrus stretch to the north for a thousand miles.

Crossing Uganda, you reach the Congo forests by way of

Lake Butiaba. This stretch is second to the mighty forests of the Amazon, though often regarded as the greatest tropical forest of the world. Not so long ago there were thought to be inexhaustible supplies of many valuable mahoganies, but from your aerial reconnaissance you will find that these regions of the Southern Provinces of Nigeria and the Congo are honeycombed with native clearings.

Follow the tropical belt to the Gulf of Guinea, and explore the mouth of the Niger, with its great inland waterways guarded by endless mangrove swamps along tidal rivers and creeks. This is the gateway to the best mahogany forest in the world. Here they are all evergreen with tree tops dazzlingly beautiful, interwoven for the greater part, though broken here and there by clearings for native farms.

Farther north in Africa is the orchard, or fringing bush, later savanna and thorn and tropical grasslands, and beyond, thousands of miles of desert. It will be difficult for you to discern where the rain forest gives place to the orchard bush, or, again, to define clearly where the orchard bush merges into the savannas, which in turn give way to the ever encroaching desert. All are progressively deteriorating; there is constant movement as desiccation hastens the march of the desert.

You will recall that these countries, once covered with thick forests, cradled civilization at its very birth. Here was the very Garden of Eden, where Man might have lived on the natural products of the forest without having recourse to nomadic farming; but he bartered his trees for goats and the flesh-pots of Egypt, forgetting that the earth was the Lord's and the fullness thereof. The earth was indeed good before man fell from his high estate.

On the next two pages:
"They stand with perfect poise on a soft forest floor."

"Fantasia" – *above*, ancient rhododendron; *right*, old cypress.

"The forest happenings of ages long gone"—wood that is 2,000 years old and still intact.

Chapter Two

FANTASIA

This is the forest primeval.

Longfellow.

PAUSE IN SPACE AND GO BACK IN TIME. EXPLORE THE genesis of life on this earth and gain a true perspective. A study of the story of the forests of the past is full of romance. How came they into being? We can but speculate on the mystery of the long journey from the birth of life from organic substance, when by a creative act lifeless matter became endowed with the properties we call life. My old Professor in Botany, Sir Albert Seward, used to say: "The difference between matter that is dead and matter that is alive cannot be adequately defined. We cannot speak of the one as motionless and inert and the other as endowed with motion and action, for all matter is in constant movement."

The study of the latest teachings of contemporary sciences leads us to believe that one day in the dim and distant past, when the temperature became favourable, organic life appeared first in warm stretches of shallow water. Later, as the outer part of the solid earth itself cooled down and became firm, it in turn provided the pre-conditions for plant and organic life.

From remotest epochs the land has striven against the encroaching seas. There have been cycles in which the land gained in the endless struggle, but such gains may have been small by comparison with land lost, which may be measured in continents. Those learned in the sciences have produced facts out of a welter of ancient traditions, and talk with confidence about cosmic cycles and make deductions for the study of the universe, which throw light on the story of our planet. Geologists and mathematicians tell us where she is left most deeply scarred by her conflict with the oceans and where land masses have been absorbed by the seas. Those of us who are unlearned in such matters have to accept these scientific deductions, but there are places in the earth where we can witness for ourselves instances of struggles between land and water, in which the land was finally victorious.

In the heart of the American continent you can gaze upon a petrified forest, where the story of the past can be reconstructed before your very eyes. Here, in a world hemmed in with many a misty mountain range and long, flat-topped mesas breakin away in terraces and steps to the plains, where the sun always shines from the bluest of skies, you can dream of past ages and interpret their story. Long before the period of cataclysmic floods, and even before the ancestral type learned to stand in the posture of man, and long, long before recorded history, great forests were growing in Arizona, just as in some parts they grow to-day. How long ago, nobody knows. Geologists may relate these petrified trees to the Triassic age, but who knows whether they have been there for one million or twenty million years? Conifers they were—that is evident to botanists and foresters, who have traced them to the same family to which the monkey-puzzle belongs. Mr. F. H. Knowlton, Botanist of the Smithsonian Institution, has identified them as *Araucarioxylon Arizonicum*. Be that as it may, in the course of time it happened that they were felled, maybe by earthquake, and there they lay on the floor of the forest, when over them swept the waters of some sea or ocean till their woody tissue was replaced with silica and became agatized. Millennia passed, and then the sea drew back. The plesiosaurus monsters became extinct, the earth heaved, craters were formed and belched forth volcanic ash and lava to shroud the story of the past. But somewhere life remained and seeds found fertile soil and earth's covering crept back in ever multiplying forms, only to retreat again before the elemental conflict.

The student of the petrified forests of the vast Northern Arizona Plateau can form some idea of the extent of the epoch-making cataclysms and prodigious events, and gain a perspective which may help him in his study of the world to-day. Let him remember that the earth, the solid surface of the earth, is forever changing its contour and that it forms waves like the sea, only infinitely more slowly. If the gradual upheavals and depressions of the earth's crust throughout millions of years were projected on a screen in the span of an hour, what a spectacle it would be! Mountains would rise in a few seconds, rocky strata would become fluid, crack, and fall in waves whose crests would tower miles in the air and sink so low that the oceans would flow over them; again rear up so high that the ocean would be drained from them.

We might observe that during the periods of subsidence the incoming waters deposited sand and silt, which in time hardened to rock of many colours, due to the presence of iron oxides. In periods of upheaval the process might be reversed, and the outgoing waters would tear at the mass and constantly strive to bear it away. We can read all this and much more, so let us examine more closely this long-buried forest and try to reconstruct its history from what we can see or read in the geological strata.

Some 10,000 feet of rock was deposited over it, and in the course of time eroded clean away. When these ancient logs were uncovered, they were found to be transformed by some magic alchemy, for Nature's chemistry had changed every one into agate and amethyst, into chalcedony and cornelian, into onyx and topaz. Here you can see thousands of acres strewn with trunks and fragments of fossilized wood of all the colours of the rainbow; millions of tons of fragments which, if polished by the lapidary, might embellish the crowns of sovereigns or delight the heart of womankind. Measure these prostrate trees and you will find that some are 200 feet in length and 7 to 10 feet in diameter. One of these huge trunks has been spared by time and spans a canyon 50 feet wide, a bridge of agate and jasper over a tree-fringed pool.

John Muir, who discovered the North Sigillaria Forest in 1906, says that the many finely preserved sigillaria, lepidodendron, and dadozylon trees here, with their peculiar roots and leaf-marks, show plainly that in this place flourished one of the noblest forests of the Carboniferous Period, and obviously the trees grew where they now lie instead of drifting in from elsewhere, for there is proof of this in the many standing stumps still visible.

This petrified forest covers many thousands of acres in five separate tracts. In several parts are the ruins of small prehistoric Indian villages, of Hopi, Zunian, and other races. Their houses of the Rainbow Forest were as original as they were beautiful, for they were built of petrified logs. Never did prehistoric builders choose more lovely stones for their habitations than the trunks of the trees which flourished ages before man began his long progress on this earth. Hammers, too, arrowheads and knives of this wood agate are often found in ruined villages hundreds of miles from the forest.

But search among the fossilized remains of trees that grew fifty million years ago, and you will see bones of the dinosaur and other creatures of the prehistoric past. From their fossilized bones and skeletons we see that their organs were developed so that they might attack and destroy each other, but their undeveloped nervous system restricted their evolution and they all, in turn, perished from the earth. Contemporary with them here and in other forest regions of the world, the great conifers were developing in size and stature, purifying the fetid air and in time making it possible for man to breathe.

The birth of protoplasm marked the beginning of the Glacial Period. Only the trained geologist can read the story of past ages as he unlocks his library with pick and shovel. The uninitiated can get little thrill from a fossilized fragment of tree or the humerus of a prehistoric reptile, which are just rocks and stones to him. He has to accept the interpretation of the past that the geologist can give him through his finds.

Paleobotanists—those skilled in identifying tree specimens from rocks or coal measures—place the period at which our forests developed recognizable modern aspects somewhere between the decline of the last dinosaur and the appearance of man. We are told, for instance, that some of the ancestors or the sequoias lived from seven to ten million years ago, and that the family was an early offshoot of the *Pinoideae* known as the *Taxodiacae*, including also the bald and Montezuma cypresses and the gingko of Japan.

Those who are skilled in the art of identifying fossilized specimens tell us that there were as many as forty-two different species of sequoias and that they were the dominant tree over much of the temperate and Arctic regions of the world until the beginning of the Glacial Period. But the descent of the ice cap, sweeping everything before it, was all but the end of that

The Tallest Tree on Earth.

The Greatest Tree on Earth.

noble line of giant trees. Only two small groups escaped and were left standing in their primeval glory. Small groups by comparison with what had been, and these were in California where they were protected by the mountain ranges of the high Sierras. There we can to-day see and touch trees of gigantic size and stature which provide a living link with geological periods.

The giant sequoias, with their cousins, the coast redwoods, have come down to us as representatives of trees that were abundant millions of years ago, as far back as Miocene times. Contemporary with the now long-vanished dinosaur, suitable vegetable companions for the great reptiles and mammals of the far-distant past, they carry with them an atmosphere, unlike the trees of other forests, which cannot be defined in words.

Thus geology is our clue to the study of prehistoric forests. There is evidence that the earliest vegetation on this planet, though of the simplest possible type, was large and lofty. The warm, damp climate would promote luxuriant growth. It is difficult to imagine what the forests of the archæan age must have been like. It would take a Walt Disney film gone mad to depict scenes in which gigantic plants and mosses and globular spore-cases on long cellular stalks, enormous mushroom growths, and fantastic toadstools of mammoth size reached up into the steamy atmosphere. Throughout all there must have been silent gloom, for no note of song-bird, buzz of insect, or rustle of leaf was there to break the endless monotony; none of these yet had being. It may have taken millennia to evolve the first pines and other primitive trees which formed the vast forests of the so-called Carboniferous Period. It was then that the forests reached their primeval glory. Nothing was more luxuriant or beautiful before, nor has it been since. The evergreen covering reached from pole to pole, for there was no ice or snow. If viewed from the stratosphere in clear atmosphere, our world must have looked like a great green star.

But the atmosphere was still damp and steamy and with an endless haze over all. Even when the sun was high overhead it could not always pierce the gloom of the forest among the aisles of pillared trunks of sigillarias, while towering overhead waved the great branches of the lepidodendrons.

When a storm broke on this forest, the branches would writhe
and toss. Mighty trees would be torn from their soft bedding
and crash, taking hundreds of trees of lesser growth to earth as
they fell. The clearings these made would soon be claimed by
younger competitors and vegetative growth, which in their day
would dominate that sphere of the forest until other hurricanes
came and in turn laid them low.

There were cataclysms upon cataclysms, followed by more
millennia, other epochs and changed climates, until the close
of the glacial periods. Such forests can now only be seen at
their best in parts of the tropics, in the high Sierras and along
the Californian coast.

Such trees as count their age in thousands of years form a
living link with the dim and distant past, when man was yet
young upon this earth. Walk through the pillared groves of
massive trees, and you will see their topmost branches pierce
the blue of the sky. They stand with perfect poise on a soft
forest floor, fern-covered. Ponderous is the strength of trunk
and limb, with almost ethereal foliage. Throughout all, the
light is ever-changing and is reflected in many colours from the
dull, soft bark, while shafts of it are reflected on the mists, and
light the ground foliage. Here, more than anywhere on earth,
we can re-live the story of the past and reconstruct the forest
happenings of ages long gone by.

Chapter Three

THE WORLD'S WONDER TREES

I will sing of the bounty of the big trees
They are the green tents of the Almighty,
He hath set them up for comfort and for shelter.

Henry van Dyke.

PIERCING THE CANOPY OF THE EVERGREEN FOREST AND pointing into the blue of the Californian sky is the tallest tree of the world. There it has stood for at least 2,000 years. Surrounded by trees of lesser growth, it has with them survived forest fires, warring Indians, ravages by pests, and depredations by man and beast, while through the centuries it has ever striven upwards in friendly rivalry with its neighbours, understanding the art of living in society and rendering mutual support and protection among its fellows. Storms there have been which have felled less flexile companions and though they have lashed its highest branches, this tree has stood—a miracle of endurance, a pinnacle of beauty, fit to summon forth the deeper feelings of man in wonderment and adoration. Its ender green foliage looked out on the world before the birth of Christ and forms a living link with the history of the past. As one touches its soft bark, contact is made with past millennia, and one's thought turns instinctively to contemplation of the meaning of life.

It is a fascinating story, 2,000 years of growth, with the tree still, as it were, in the prime of life, yielding myriads of fertile seeds and scattering its progeny in profusion. All this time it has shown a rhythm in growth completing the circle of life. In the secret of its heart each year it has recorded its history, which one day may be read in its rings.

This tree is just one of millions in a great green belt which sweeps the Pacific Coast from the borders of Oregon to the Golden Gate. It is the dominating species of this primeval forest which had its beginning when man was young upon the earth; it has witnessed the evolution of man and played its part in producing the life-giving oxygen that he breathes, clearing the fetid swamps where but dinosaurs and prehistoric reptiles held sway. This forest at one time encompassed the Northern Hemisphere, and forty-two of its species are recorded in fossilized remains. In other parts of the earth it was destroyed by the ice cap, while here it remains as a record of past glory.

The world does not yet know how nearly this green mantle was swept from its last sanctuary. But for the devotion and self-sacrificing ideal of a few friends, these great trees might have followed the fate of their brethren farther south and have been engulfed in logging operations. But after nine years of endeavour, an area of 12,000 acres has been set aside, and there is a still further project of adding to this a Tribute Grove of 5,000 acres, a fitting memorial to those who, for an ideal, made the supreme sacrifice.

This coast redwood, *Sequoia sempervirens*, is standing on North Dyerville Flat in the Humboldt State, Redwood Park, near several others which closely vie with it. But after searching the world over and comparing my figures of the tallest trees on earth with those of other experts in various countries, I give this noble coast redwood first place for height, for it is 364 feet high and 18 feet in diameter at 4½ feet above the ground.

When I first made its acquaintance in 1932, on a world tour in search of the most interesting trees, it had already been measured by two engineers, who found another tree 361 feet high and 14 feet in diameter at breast height, and yet another, east of the Redwood Highway between Dyerville Bridge and the south end of the Flat, which was 353 feet in height with a diameter of 15 feet breast-high. There was yet another on Bull Creek Flat 347 feet high and 16 feet in diameter, breast-high. Nowhere in the world have I seen so many trees in close proximity which vied with each other in attaining such a dizzy height. How can I convey what this means? Stand this redwood by St. Paul's Cathedral, and its top would reach the crest of the dome. Plant it in the deepest part of the North Sea, and its highest branches would wave above the water. Place it by the Statue of Liberty, and it would tower over the flaming torch.

In my search for taller trees, I have come across many claims for trees whose pre-eminence in height has competed in vain. I have listened to fabulous figures given me by tree-fellers and lumbermen who clamoured for the honour of having seen or felled taller trees. Interested as I was to hear stories of pre-existing trees from 400 to 500 feet in height, I could find no living evidence anywhere which would prove that they existed. It might, of course, be argued from existing stumps of great trees that their tops were proportionately higher than any in the world to-day, but figures show that those greater in girth or diameter are not necessarily greater in height.

The botanical range of *Sequoia sempervirens* extends from a few scattered groups of trees along the Chetco River in Southern Oregon southward in a long, narrow belt to other scattered groups south of Mendocino County, California. The belt is about 1,500 miles long, reaching an extreme width of thirty-five miles in Mendocino County, and averaging about eighteen miles. The total extent of the coast redwood area is about two million acres. It occurs from sea level to an altitude of 2,500 feet.

This species occupies a temperature range extending from slightly below freezing to a maximum of about 100°. The rain-fall varies from 20 to 60 inches. But the most important factor in the growth of the coast redwood is that its range lies almost wholly within the fog belt. The effect of fog in cutting down summer evaporation and reducing soil evaporation is the most important influence in the distribution of these tall trees.

The coast redwoods provide, in fact, the tallest tree from among their ranks, whereas high up on the western slopes of the Sierra Nevada, from the American River on the north to Deer Creek on the south, and between elevations of 4,000 to 8,000 feet, are the Big Trees—the *greatest* trees on earth.

The highest living big tree in the Calerveras Grove in the Sierra Nevada Mountains was recorded to be 325 feet. Though I have visited the most famous giants, I have not found any much over 300 feet in height. The height of the biggest tree measured was actually 273·9 feet, though it had a base cir-cumference of 102·7 feet. Its greatest base diameter was 37·3 feet, its mean base diameter 32·7 feet, while 8 feet above the ground it measured 27·4 feet. At 100 feet above the ground it was still 18·7 feet in diameter. At about 150 feet from the ground

C

a huge branch came out and went up for 130 feet, and where it left the tree its diameter was 7·3 feet. The total weight of this tree is estimated, according to U.S.A. Park Service computation, to be over 12,000,000 lb. or 6,167 tons, this weight being divided as follows: trunk 11,204,220 lb.; limbs 356,640 lb.; root system 749,760 lb.; bark 15,579 lb.; foliage 9,440 lb.; total 12,335,639 lb.—and that mighty giant has sprung from a tiny seed half the size of the head of a match. A miracle of growth indeed, which must be a challenge to trees the world over. That tree is known as General Sherman, and it is situated in the Sequoia National Park. The coast redwood is taller and so probably are the eucalyptus and perhaps other trees, but there are none to challenge the bulk of the big trees of the high Sierras.

There are legends of even greater giants, but there is little information concerning heights of pre-existent sequoias. Undoubtedly there have been larger trees than the General Sherman. Just south of General Grant Park, in what is known as the Big Stump Basin, there are several stumps of trees that have been destroyed by fire or by lumbering which are at least 25 feet in diameter several feet above the ground. But these are bare of bark and so must have been considerably larger, for the thickness of bark on the big trees varies from 8 inches to 4 feet. There is one stump in the Calaveras North Grove which has been used as a dance floor by as many as thirty-two couples at a time. This is thought to be the historical tree discovered by Dowd, a miner of Murphy's Camp, who lost his way when hunting and found himself in the kingdom of the giants.

No other conifer blooms so profusely as the big tree. In late January and February it first flowers, the millions of blossoms at the tips of its finger-like foliage clustering so thickly that they change the colour of the tree. The flowers are heavily laden with golden pollen, and they dust the entire tree when ripe, turning it to gold, while they cover the snow at its feet with golden dust. In May and June the cones begin to form: these are little pearly grey objects, somewhat smaller than a grain of wheat; but after three weeks they become a brilliant grass-green colour, and by the end of the summer they have reached about one-third of their full size. Cones do not mature until the close of their second summer, when they throw out myriads of tiny seeds. When fully-grown, the cone is from 2 inches to 3¾ inches long, and from 1 inch to 2½ inches thick, and is composed of thirty to forty closely-packed scales. At the base of each scale are three to eight seeds embedded in a reddish pigment. The seeds are ⅛ inch in length.

It is obvious that a big tree will bear millions of seeds, but only one in a million reaches maturity. Quality, not quantity, is their motto; only so are they able to develop their gigantic stature and reign supreme in the kingdom of trees. The wonder of it is that seeds from a tree 4,000 years old produce as vigorous progeny as those from a mere stripling of 500 or 1,000 years. The vitality of the big tree impresses one as much as its size, its majesty, and its colour.

Unlike the coast redwood, which can reproduce itself from stool shoots, the big tree reproduces only from seed. But their fertility is low compared with other conifers, and the young trees have many enemies. In the virgin forests the most favourable conditions for growth occur only at long intervals, and then only in certain localities. No sooner are the seedlings above ground than destruction and disaster assail them, so that few survive the first year. Birds, such as sparrows and finches, are attracted to the tender green plants with the seed hulls on their tops, and pick off the topmost portions for food. This invariably kills the plant. Cutworms destroy others, and large black wood ants levy a heavy toll by cutting off the plants and dragging them into their nests. Rodents, such as ground squirrels and chipmunks, destroy large numbers by eating off the tender tops. Many of the plants take root in places where the soil is either too wet or too dry, and they soon perish. So it may be seen that the first year's life of the big tree is a precarious one, and very few of the many thousand plants that germinate survive.

Some seeds of the sequoia have found their way to other countries, where they grow and flourish. In 1854 many were planted in England, small transplants being distributed by nurserymen and sold at £5 each. Some of these have already attained a height of about 150 feet. In New Zealand the big

trees grow much faster than in their native habitat, and in time
it is possible that they will outstrip their forebears in the high
Sierras.

Whereas the big tree, *Sequoia gigantia*, is the world's largest
tree, and the coast redwood, *Sequoia sempervirens*, is the world's
tallest tree, the Montezuma cypress, *Taxodium Mucronatum*
(*Sabino* in Spanish, or *Ahuehuete* in Aztec), is the world's largest
diameter tree. "Arbol de Montezuma", the largest in this
grove, is 45 feet in diameter and 200 feet high and was centuries
old at the time of conquest. The grove is located at the base of
the rising ground upon which stands the castle, the ancient
seat of the Inca monarchs and summer residence of most of the
Spanish viceroys and presidents of the Republic. These were
protected and cared for through centuries by the Mexicans,
and before them by the Aztecs, so that they could receive
water during their youth until their roots could penetrate to
underground water supplies, when they could fend for themselves. At the time of the conquest of Mexico by Cortés, the
cypress was much more widely distributed than to-day. The
extension of agriculture and mining following Spanish occupation resulted in the destruction of most of the forests. But
fortunately, the Spaniards saved the more outstanding of these
grand trees, and, as with the Californian redwoods, there seems
to be no natural age limit to the Montezuma cypress. There are
over 200 splendid specimens in the park surrounding the
Castle of Chapultepec, two miles south-west of the city of
Mexico.

The most remarkable of all Montezuma cypresses grows
in the walled garden of a church in the village of Santa Maria
del Tule, in the southern Mexican state of Oaxaca, near the
capital city of the same name. "El Tule", as the tree is affec-
tionately called, is enormous, and has a base diameter of 47
feet, while above the buttresses it is 41 feet. Its trunk and crown
are unquestionably the largest of any evergreen tree in the
world. It is buttressed at the base, and at about 50 feet from
the ground it branches into huge limbs, forming a rounded
domed crown. When the sun is at its height it throws a shadow
of 15,000 square feet, equal to a circle of 140 feet in diameter.
This tree is 160 feet high. It is impossible to estimate its age,

"I have visited the most famous giants."

The Sanctuary of the Woods, North of Dyerville.

but there have been many guesses, which range from 3,000 to 10,000 years. All estimates are mostly conjectures, and the 4,000 rings of the sequoias actually counted by John Muir place them as the authentically oldest trees on earth.

Other countries vie with the American continent, for they, too, have their wonder trees. In the Waipoua Forest, New Zealand, are the giant kauris, *Araucaria australis*, with their massive boles which tower without taper for a hundred feet clear of branches. Smooth as a marble column, the trunks of kauri are different from any other tree on earth. The largest measured was 17 feet in diameter, containing 214,000 feet board measures with a probable age of 1,200 to 1,400 years. The largest recorded tree was 22 feet in diameter, with an age of 2,200 years.

The eucalyptus trees of Australia are greater in height than the kauris, and may be the second tallest trees in the world. They provide a greater number of varieties than any other timber tree, for there are over two hundred and thirty species.

The Douglas fir, *Pseudotsuga douglasii*, of British Columbia, Vancouver Island, and the Pacific Coast southwards, has been described as the world's greatest timber tree, one being measured with a base diameter of 15 feet 4 inches, while the tallest fir, at Ryderwood, Washington, is 324 feet 4 inches; the age of the oldest recorded is 1,400 years.

The world's largest pine is the sugar pine, *Pinus lambertiana*. David Douglas reported his discovery of a tree at Umpqua, Oregon, as 18 feet 4 inches in diameter, and total length of 245 feet. The greatest recorded age is 600 years.

The bald cypress, *Taxodium distichum*, has been described as the wood eternal. Its habitat is the South Atlantic and the Gulf coastal region, and it is the largest American tree east of the Rocky Mountains. The one known as the "Senator", near Longwood, Florida, has a maximum diameter of $17\frac{1}{2}$ feet, and mean diameter of 15 feet. Its height is 125 feet, and its age has been guessed at 3,000 years.

The world's largest cedar is the western red, *Thuja plicata*, and it is to be found on the Hoh River, Washington. It is approximately 20 feet in diameter, 160 feet high, and may be from 800 to 1,000 years old.

There are other trees which rival each other in height, form and beauty. For instance, the world's largest spruce tree attains the height of 230 feet, with a maximum diameter of 14 feet. This is the *Picea sitchensis*, or tideland spruce. There is the western juniper, *Juniperus occidentalis*, described as the most beautiful conifer wood. It grows in northern California, with a maximum diameter of 21 feet 6 inches, and a height of 80 feet. Its age is probably from 2,000 to 3,000 years. The Formosa cedar, *Chamaecyparis formosiensis*, is the largest Asiatic conifer, known in its native land as "Benihi". The Biblical cedar of Lebanon, *Cedrus libani*, the largest of which stands in the Bsharri Grove, Lebanon, is a very old tree. The temple tree of Japan, *Cryptomeria japonica*, holds the honour of providing the world's grandest tree memorial. There is an avenue of forty miles at Mikko, Japan, planted by a poor prince over 300 years ago.

Many wonderful specimens are to be found in the ranks of the broad-leaved trees, such as the sweet or Spanish chestnut, the oak, the beech, the mahogany, the baobab, the camphor trees, while the banyan or sacred fig has been known to cover an extent of 4 acres. It is said that the olive tree never dies, but continues to throw up root shoots long after the trunk of an old tree has decayed. The gingko can trace back its unchanged form through the millions of years, for it was indeed one of the first family of trees.

Chapter Four

THE TREE OF LIFE

He sendeth into their bodies the sap of life,
They lift themselves lightly toward the heavens,
They rejoice in the broadening of their branches.

Henry van Dyke.

IT IS WITH AWE AND REVERENCE THAT A FELLOW CREATURE in God's creation attempts to describe one of his elder brethren. In this machine age a tree has been likened to a most delicate machine, but no machine invented by man can compete with the living tree, which runs itself, repairs itself, maintains itself, and re-creates itself.

The average person may think of plants and trees as things of beauty, and in a vague sort of way realize their usefulness; but little does he understand the complicated workings of that intricate system. We are advised to "consider the lilies of the field, how they grow; they toil not, neither do they spin"—how much more, then, should we marvel at the growth of a tree.

It is a miracle of growth from seed to maturity. From the kindly darkness of the earth, where germination takes place, the shoot and root progress in opposite directions, the former drawn towards the light, the latter digging into mother earth for sustenance. The root explores for moisture, and sends out little branch roots in search of food, which stimulates the up-ward growth. The shoot in its turn sends out branches, and through the activity of the cambium, or growing layer, the stem thickens. Supplied with a few mineral salts, water, and air, the tree builds up its body, increasing in size as year by year it adds a layer of tissue to its growth. The essential chemical processes continue under the influence of sunlight, and, by reason of its unique power of utilizing radiant energy from the sun, the tree obtains carbon for the manufacture of carbohydrates and proteins.

The green leaves which clothe the tree may be likened to the laboratories where carbohydrates and proteins are made, for

all the processes of growth take place in them. They build up
the framework and add fuel for the maintenance of respiration
and the working activities of the whole tree; thus life and
growth depend upon the leaves. Delicate indeed is the mechanism of the stomata through which respiration takes place, and
there may be hundreds of these minute openings on a single
leaf. A hole made by a sharp needle is large in comparison
with the size of a stomatal opening. Generally speaking, they
are open during the day and shut or partially shut during the
night. In a single day a birch tree may give off in vapour
through its leaves about $15\frac{1}{2}$ gallons of water, and on a very
hot day as much as 80 gallons may be pumped into the air.
It is not only aqueous vapour that passes through the stomata
into the external air: the living cells of the tree are constantly
giving off carbon dioxide in respiration. On the other hand, it
is through the stomata that the leaf receives supplies of oxygen
from the outer air; this diffuses into the air spaces between the
leaf-cells, and is thus available for setting into operation the
essential chemical changes by which the energy stored in
carbon compounds is liberated and rendered available as a
factor in operating the whole tree machinery. But most important of all, and the greatest service of the leaf, in which the
stomata take a leading part, is the function of absorbing
carbon dioxide from the outer air which is to be used for the
manufacture of sugars. As the carbon dioxide reaches the wet
cells within a leaf, it is dissolved in the water which saturates
the cell walls, and thence passes in solution through the walls
into the living protoplasm containing chloroplasts.

The chloroplasts are well-defined but minute specks of protoplasm which hold in their substance the chlorophyll; this
is the substance which gives the green colour to leaves. Small
as the chloroplasts are, they are able to absorb an amount of
light sufficient to enable a tree to manufacture a large bulk of
carbon-containing compounds. There are about 400,000
chloroplasts in a square millimetre of a leaf. When we consider
that a well-grown elm tree has seven million leaves, and that
this represents a surface of 22,834,000 square inches as the
total area in a tree, the total chloroplast area in such a tree
would be 456,680,000 yards or 94,355 acres or 147·4 square

miles. Surely this is an amazing example of mass co-operation. But without this co-operation the tree would not grow. This is the process by which the cells are built up in the tree. It is difficult to form any idea of the speed at which the cells are produced; but if a man were to *count* cells all day and night at 200 a minute, or 105,120,000 in a year, in round numbers he would be able to count 200 million cells in nineteen centuries. Taking the average size of a cell as $\frac{1}{10}$ millimetre, and estimating the number of cells per square millimetre at 100 to 10,000 per square centimetre, he would have counted the cells up to a height of 20 centimetres, that is less than a foot in a single tree of the forest after his strenuous labour extending over 1,900 years.

Although we can with comparative ease gauge the chemical contents of the ingredients which go to make up the cells of a tree, their form and quality remain a mystery. How is it, for instance, that the ash takes from the earth and air the elements necessary to form the character and texture of its wood, or the shape of its leaves, or colour of its bark? Other trees growing on the same soil contrive to develop entirely different characteristics. These are mysteries which are yet to be explained.

Another miracle is the manner by which trees cable themselves to the earth and maintain their poise while continually tapping subterranean supplies of water. The roots of a tree serve a double purpose, for while anchoring the tree and providing a mechanical service, they actively take in water, though it is only the younger and more delicate parts of the root system which do this. The actual tip of the root is covered with a protective cap of cells which is constantly worn away as it rubs against solid particles in the soil. With the aid of its *pileorhiza*, it will pass, not merely through crumbling soil, but through stony strata. How is it that so soft a substance can penetrate hard bodies which we break through only by means of a great effort of strength, using tools yet harder? Another mystery, this, how a root without external aid can split obstacles against which man has to employ steel and stone.

The root tips are provided with remarkable osmotic apparatus for the purpose of taking up water and mineral food from the soil. The most important source of water for the tree is the moisture found between the solid particles of the soil. This is composed of water particles, some of which can be easily moved, others only with more difficulty. To the former belongs the water which drops from the sample of soil when it is squeezed, while to the latter the water which may still be present even in a comparatively dry soil. The whole sheaf of cells bears the name of *primary root cortex*, and it is destined to serve as the first place of reception for the fluid absorbed by the root hairs. The cortex of the root represents a living reservoir for the liquid taken up by the root hairs, in which larger quantities are accommodated, as well as in the narrow cavities of the epidermal cells. The water channels leading upwards, which draw upon the reservoir, become in this way to a certain extent independent of irregularities to which the activity of the hairs is exposed.

The water, drawn from the depths of the earth, continues to rise by osmotic pressure unchecked through each breathing cell and sieve-tube, by way of the growing layer, until it reaches the topmost leaves of the tree. After circulating in the leaves and giving of itself, it absorbs valuable ingredients from the air and returns once more to the depths of the roots, having built up the xylem, or new wood. The xylem is the mass of material to which the cambium gives rise on the side towards the pith in stems, twigs, and roots. At first a cell shed off by the cambium towards the pith hardly begins to differ from its sisters in its growth; but then there also begins a chemical change of its cellulose membrane which is generally finished in the same growing season. This is known as *lignification*. Lignified cell walls are generally more or less strongly thickened and stratified.

The most important seats of life in tree stems are the cambium and the rind. Living constituents extend from there only into the sap wood, and their bulk is small compared with that of the dead membranes which form the conducting tissues, and the fibres which serve for the rigidity of the whole structure of the tree. The living cells of the wood act as stores for that part of the food materials, formed in the leaves, which does not find immediate use in the growing points or in the cambium. These materials are collected in the form of starch or fatty oil.

These together form a continuous network through the wood, of which one constituent, the wood parenchyma, forms lines running parallel with the boundaries of the annual rings (tangential) and is often only visible under the microscope or a strong lens; while the other—the radially directed medullary rays—is easily seen in many kinds of wood.

In all trees, the bast, or inner bark (the phloem) consists of sieve-tubes which in broad-leaved trees always appear in company with companion cells—bast parenchyma and cambiform cells. These elements together form the soft bast. To the hard bast belong the bast fibres and other sclerenchymatous cells. The medullary rays also, in so far as they extend into the bast, are, in trees, to be assigned to the bast and not to the ground tissue, as they are formed only from cambium cells.

It may be noticed that the fresh green colour of the young twig tends to give place to a brown one towards the end of the summer. This change is due to the replacement of the epidermis of the shoot by a periderm which possesses the protective properties of the epidermis, but in an enhanced degree. The periderm arises through the cells of the green rind-parenchyma immediately adjacent to the epidermis, beginning to divide parallel with the surface of the twig. The daughter cells cut off towards the outside become cork cells, those towards the inside of the twig becoming cells of the green rind-parenchyma, and between these two kinds of products there remains a sheath of cells capable of division after the manner of the cambium. This is called the cork cambium or phellogen.

The hardness of a bark or a cork depends upon the form of the cell walls of its elements. If the latter are thin-walled and with large lumina, sponge cork is formed, such as in the English elm, robinia, and spindle tree. The cell walls of such sponge corks sometimes consist in part of cellulose. The cork of *Quercus suber*, the cork oak, and *Quercus occidentalis*, to which we owe sheet cork, belong to this class. The name "stone bark" is given to bark formations which are very hard in consequence of the great thickness of the walls of their elements. Raggedness of the surface of the bark is caused by the stretching of the rind associated with the growth in thickness of the stem of the tree. Theoretically the bulk on the outside of the cambium is as

great as that on the inside, but in many species weather conditions cause flakes to come off. The London plane is an
example of a tree which sheds its bark each year.

The growing tissues of the tree continue to communicate
with the outside world through air passages, the lenticels, in its
bark, and through these it breathes. One reason why certain
trees will not flourish in cities or industrial areas is that
these breathing passages become fouled with the smoke and
dirt.

Externally we can watch a tree grow: we see the buds
breaking into leaf, shoot, or flower, the branches lengthening
and the trunk expanding; but little do we know of the secret
life inside the tree. The sudden awakening of the tree in spring
suggests that the rising temperature does not find the internal
economy of the tree unprepared. It is a fact that what is to be
unfolded at the beginning of the next growing season has
already been initiated, as in the heart of a seed the form of the
mature tree may be seen. In the secrecy of its heart, each tree
keeps a record in ring-shaped markings which may be seen on
the surface of the cross section of a felled tree. These marks
are the expression of seasonal variations, in the mode of
formation of the wood of the tree, which correspond to the
change from one vegetation period to another. The elements of
the wood formed at the beginning of the period of growth
activity are of a different character from those which are
formed later, and the differences which are present between the
last wood of a period and the first of the following one are in
most species so great that they are evident to the naked eye.
These are popularly known as the annual rings, but there have
been cases in which several rings appear during one year, as,
for instance, in an oak which has been attacked by defoliating
caterpillars. Bared of leaves, growth is retarded as in winter, to
be continued when the new leaves appear.

The tree is man's best friend and one of God's noblest crea-
tions. How dependent we are upon trees has yet to be fully
realized. Only in a vague sort of way can we assess the real
contribution that trees make to human existence on this planet.
Their functions are legion and their life is interwoven with
earth and ether. To the trees we owe the quality of our food,

General Grant Tree.

Douglas fir, British Columbia.

the quantity of our water, and the purity of the very air we breathe.

The Psalmist appreciated the balance of Nature and the place of the tree in relation to the whole: "He watereth the hills from His chambers: the earth is satisfied with the fruit of Thy works. He causeth the grass to grow for the cattle, and herb for the service of man: that he may bring forth food out of the earth; and wine that maketh glad the heart of man, and oil to make his face shine, and bread which strengtheneth man's heart. The trees of the Lord are full of sap; the cedars of Lebanon, which He hath planted; where the birds make their nests: as for the stork, the fir-trees are her house. . . . O Lord, how manifold are Thy works! in wisdom hast Thou made them all: the earth is full of Thy riches."

Chapter Five

THE RHYTHM OF THE FOREST

My heart is awed within me, when I think
Of the great miracle that still goes on,
In silence, round me—the perpetual work
Of Thy creation, finished, yet renewed
Forever.

Bryant.

A FOREST IS A SOCIETY OF LIVING THINGS, THE GREATEST OF which is the tree. In a virgin forest, growth keeps pace with decay: at one place a tree will be reaching maturity, at another declining. As an old tree falls, a gap is made in the canopy, light is let in, and many younger trees race with each other to occupy this new opening. This is happening by slow degrees throughout the forest, and so the rhythm of growth is maintained.

It has taken centuries to form the floor of the forest. Up to ninety per cent of mineral soils is derived from rocks by a process of what is called weathering, which is carried on by alternate freezing and thawing, contraction and expansion, as a result of cold and heat, the action of water and carbonic acid, and the prying action of roots.

It is possible that a forest of to-day may be standing on a site which at one time was bare rock. Perhaps some lichens established themselves on a damp level surface of the rock. The weathering action of the elements disintegrated the surface and formed a layer of tiny rock particles. This process was hastened by the chemical secretions of the lichens until these mosses were followed by grasses and in due order by herbs and shrubs; and then one day a wind-borne tree seed lodged there and began to grow, and thus founded a community of trees. That was how the forest began. Tiny alpine species they must have been, but their leaves provided the first litter, and in the course of further centuries the way was prepared for higher types of forest. As the treed area developed, precipitation increased, growth was hastened as well as decay, acting and re-acting upon the future generations of trees. In all this, fungi and bacteria played their part in producing and modifying humus and litter. Parent trees scattered their seed, which, borne by the wind, colonized fresh areas.

Each group of seedlings contended with the others for light, and the suppressed and less fortunate in the race fed the growth of their victors. The trees which attained their full growth shared the sky and sunlight with their neighbours for a brief space after so long a struggle. Practically all trees make their best growth in full sunlight, but there are those more particularly adapted to survive in partial shade; these may form a second story, their foliage being more dense than the light-demanders. All trees are more tolerant of shade when they are young. It is the crowding of trees in the forest which helps them in their upward growth and kills off the lower branches, making the timber free from knots.

There is continual decline as well as growth in the forest. There is no standing still: as soon as a tree stops growing it begins to decline. Even before this, decay may have set in within its heart, and it is set upon by beetles and borers, its roots are attacked by fungi, its huge body is no longer supported, and a mere gust of wind may bring it to earth. It becomes a home for woodlice and millions of insects, which play their part in returning the fallen tree to the earth from which it sprang.

The forest floor is the name given to the ground beneath the trees in a forest. The mulch is made up from fallen twigs and leaves which remain on the ground, where they slowly decay and form a cover of rich mould or humus. This protective covering forms a most useful purpose: it permits the rain and snow waters to permeate the soil without making it too compact, thus allowing the air to penetrate, while at the same time it prevents the washing away of the land and too rapid or exces-sive evaporation from the surface. The humus also assists the decomposition of the mineral substances in the soil, which in turn provide food for the growing trees. Tree growth is less dependent on the condition of the surface soil than it is upon the depth of the subsoil. It has been shown that trees are not exacting on the quality of soils because they make their own manure and fertilize themselves, and even provide a surplus.

Whenever man has sought for land to grow food, he has found it in the forest. The story of colonization is that of clearing the forest to make farms. So long as the farms were kept small and tree-surrounded, fertility was maintained, the trees afforded protection for the crops, modified the temperature in both summer and winter, and provided nesting-places for helpful birds which destroyed harmful insects. Above all, the land was enriched by the humus with its mycorrhizal associations—the secret of successful growth.

Once the virgin forest is exploited by man, it is necessary to introduce cultural operations to maintain the highest standard of yield. The resulting thickets of fresh growth must be thinned, the mature timber harvested. This is the art of silviculture.

From the forester's point of view, the most important thing is to fit each species into the most suitable habitat. This calls for a knowledge of the factors of habitat, such as moisture, temperature, light, and soil, the requirements of each species and the demand that it makes upon Nature. These requirements are discovered in the first instance through nursery practice. Seeds are sown under varying conditions approximating to the natural forest where they grow. Whole series are provided, and the results carefully observed and tabulated. It would be simple if in Nature trees grew in pure formation, but it has been found by experiment that a combination of species tends to give the best results. Certain nurse trees may be required to assist growth in the early stages, while at later stages another combination of helpful trees is needed to bring the main crop to maturity. Whereas light is an important *silvical* factor, so also is root competition. The forester is concerned with more than what he sees happening above the ground, for he has to estimate the condition of root growth. But it is reasonable for him to presume that where the crown canopy is denser the root competition will be more severe; therefore the density of the shade should also be an indication of the intensity of the root competition.

The beneficial influences of a forest are many. Trees are forever working for man's good. During the day the ground under

The Rhythm of Growth.

Broken Rhythm.

the trees is protected from the sun's rays and is therefore cooler than soil unprotected. As a result of this protection, the forest air is cooler than the air in the open, and, as air is in constant circulation, this tends to reduce the temperature on hot days. At night trees retard the radiation of heat from the ground under them. This helps to equalize the temperature. To anyone flying over a forest in the daytime the upward motion of hot air which has been driven into the forest from the surrounding plains is quite perceptible, while at night there is a reverse process which tends to drag the plane down over any extensive forest area.

This same pull may help to precipitate clouds and increase rainfall in that neighbourhood. Trees may increase horizontal precipitation, while their leaves retain the moisture, preventing a quick run-off to the ground below. It takes time for the rain storm to penetrate the leaves, and still longer for it to percolate through the humus, and longer yet to find its way through the root channels to the subsoil, where later it will form springs, which in turn will feed rivers. Evaporation is retarded first by the covering afforded by the shade of the leaves, and, secondly by the blanket of humus forming the forest floor, thus keeping the water level high. It is one of the most valuable functions of the forest to provide catchment areas, and so distribute water for growing crops.

The water capital of the earth may be thought of as consisting of two parts, the fixed capital and the circulating capital. The first consists not only of the water stored in the earth, but also of that in the atmosphere. The circulating capital is that which is evaporated from water surfaces, from the soil and from vegetation, and which, after having been temporarily held in the atmosphere in the form of clouds, is returned again as rain, dew, or snow. The function of the trees is to filter the water and distribute it, and forest cover directly influences the pattern of this distribution.

We cannot yet clearly follow the intricacies of the circulation of water on the earth, in the earth, in the trees, in the ocean, and in the air, but we do know that man's ignorant interference with the forest and other cover has greatly reduced the earth's fertility and is still doing so. The natural circulation of

D

water is a subject which must have our careful study and deepest consideration.

The very life of man—the food that he eats, the air that he breathes, and the water that he drinks—is bound up with the forest; he is dependent on the forest, and its cycle must be maintained. The catastrophes that have occurred, such as the dust bowl of the Middle West, the flooding of the Mississippi Valley, the famines of China, the droughts of Australia, and the march of the deserts of Equatorial Africa, have been caused when man has broken this cycle.

We can now understand why forests are the ideal covering for the earth, for they maintain the right soil conditions for plant growth, the litter of leaves, twigs, and branches shed by the trees completely covering the ground. This litter may be only two inches in depth or it may be a foot or more, but the effect is the same. Its first function is to keep the soil from being washed away, but second only to this in importance is that it retains moisture and rain water, which, instead of running off, seeps slowly into the earth, to come up later in the form of springs. This economy preserves the soil in the necessary condition to fulfil its major purpose of producing plant and food growth.

Above the forest floor there are various strata or layers of tree life. In the forest the crowns of the dominant trees form the uppermost stratum; the next may be formed by trees of lesser height; then come the larger shrubs, and, lower still, herbs and, in damp climates, mosses. In English woodlands there are usually four strata, but in the tropical rain forests there are as many as six distinct layers of tree growth. In the lower and middle zones is a tangled mass of woody lianas which weave their strands from tree to tree, often dragging them to earth and thus making the cover more impenetrable. You will understand then how the earth's surface is protected from the torrential downpours, which, but for this protection, would wash the soil away, leaving rock and sand in their wake.

As a forest officer in Equatorial Africa, I have had an opportunity of studying the rapid deterioration that is taking place in forest types. I have seen the forest climax reached where superb trees vie with each other in the battle of terrific growth and where the forest has reached perfection. I have seen this same area invaded by nomadic farmers who have cleared away the growth of ages and sacrificed some of the most valuable timber in the world, burning it to make ash in which to grow their yams. I have marched for days along forest trails through what to the casual observer might have appeared to be primeval forest, but upon closer examination I found that the whole of this area was pock-marked with clearings. The rhythm had been broken—never again would that forest attain its former glory.

As I travelled northwards from the province of Benin, the forest became more open. I left the tropical evergreen rain forest and soon began to encounter secondary growth. This country was once farmland cut from the virgin forest, and now and again are to be seen tall old trees, remnants of high forest standing out in the open grass. Throughout all this area there is constant change, for the equilibrium of the forest has been upset. Northwards the deterioration is seen to be more rapid. Almost without warning a new zone is entered where the grass towers six feet or more—cruel, harsh grass which tears at one's boots and makes going slow and difficult. Here I encountered the first fan palms, a sure sign that I was approaching the desert. As the grass becomes shorter the flat-topped desert thorns appear, and there is evidence of many fires in the charred stems of the dwarfed trees. Soon the degraded grass ceases to be able to support animal life, so the nomads cut the tops of the scrub trees to feed their goats, and thus bring about the final extinction of the savanna forest. It is here that the encroaching desert becomes spectacular. The wind-blown sand often reduces visibility to a few yards; its continual movement is a terrifying thing, for man no longer has the power to control this demon which he has let loose. Here indeed is the final result of broken rhythm. The natural forest has not been allowed to resuscitate and heal the scars inflicted by man. When earth's green covering has been removed, the land becomes inhospitable to man and beast, the rainfall lessens until the clouds steadily pass by, leaving the earth parched and dry. Away to the north of the Gold Coast, in the French sphere of influence, for years the nomadic farmers have been literally driven before the oncoming desert. The moving sands have buried their sparse crops and are racing them into the narrow wedge of forest that remains. Here may be witnessed racial suicide on a bigger scale than the world has ever before seen. Knowing the end of the forest to be near, and with little chance of growing food, the chiefs have forbidden marriage, and the women refuse to bear children, for they will not raise sons and daughters for starvation.

Chapter Six

A NEW SAHARA

The hills lie bare, no seeds for growth—
Fallen the forest trees
And winds, haunting the lonely space
Mourn for the sons of these.

Edith Livingston Smith.

ALTHOUGH IT HAS TAKEN CLOSE ON 2,000 YEARS TO CREATE the great Sahara of Africa, it has taken but two centuries to form the Dust Bowl of America. This has been made possible by the invention of the internal combustion engine, modern warfare, and the greed of man.

Three hundred years ago settlers from England arrived in the North American continent and established themselves at Plymouth and at Jamestown. Around them was nothing but forest. They cut trees to make log cabins, and lived on the natural foods of the forest; there were wild fruits and nuts in plenty, and they hunted game. Like the nomadic farmers of Africa, they made clearings with axe and fire for their farms. To these settlers the forest was an enemy to be overcome, and they waged ruthless war upon the trees. From the earliest days of their settlement the home country called upon them for pine and spruce masts for her ships, and for fine oak timber for the hulls of Britain's growing Navy. This was the beginning of the lumber industry. For 100 years the white pine of the New England forests was sacrificed to build the houses of the growing colony. This was the beginning of the reckless career of lumbering which exposed the land to erosion and left ruined townships in its wake.

When the white pine of New England was exhausted, the lumbermen waded into the forests of New York, and by 1850 that was the leading lumber-producing state of America. In ten short years those forests in turn became exhausted, for they were cut without any consideration for the future. As soon as the timber was gone, the mills moved on, leaving derelict towns where once had lived prosperous communities. By 1860 Pennsylvania was the foremost State in lumber-production and forest destruction. That State, originally known as Sylvania because of its unrivalled virgin forests, and then named after William Penn, was soon exploited.

The lumbermen next invaded the Lake States of Michigan, Wisconsin, and Minnesota, where they found dense stands of white pine easy of access and close to water transport. Here indeed was a grand opportunity of exploitation on a scale un-dreamt of in the previous history of lumbering. Bigger and better mills became the order of the day; thousands of hands were recruited, big towns sprang up like mushrooms in the night, and vast fortunes were made by harvesting the growth of the ages.

It was in the lumber camps of the Lake States that the legend-ary figure of Paul Bunyan arose. He was of French-Canadian origin, and crossed over into the United States in "the spring following the winter of the blue snow". Paul Bunyan was re-puted to be of such proportions that he used a charred pine tree for a pencil. His inseparable companion and helpmate was Babe, his blue ox, which measured forty-two axe handles and had a plug of tobacco between his horns. So big was Paul Bunyan's shot-gun that in an emergency he used its barrels as smoke stacks for his mills. He fought a battle in Upside-Down Mountain with Hels Helson, the Wild Bull of the Woods, and the dust they stirred up settled and formed the Black Hills of South Dakota.

The legendary figure of Paul Bunyan has become a symbol of the ruthless exploitation of the forest, showing man's lust for wealth regardless of the next generation.

It looked as though the forests of the Lake States were in-exhaustible, but in sixty years they were as efficiently wiped out as those of New England, New York, and Pennsylvania. The mills, starved for the want of timber, were deserted or dismantled, or moved on with their hordes of workmen. Fires roared through the masses of dry slash left on the ground, and even the few parent trees which might have yielded seed for a new forest were more often than not reduced to ashes. The sandy land was too poor to farm, and bleak desolation ranged from Detroit to Dakota.

Meanwhile, by 1900, a new lumber boom had started, this time in the south. In another ten years it had reached its height. Having depleted these areas of rich pine, the man with the axe turned to the west, harvested ponderosa pine in the Rocky Mountain region, cleaned up what he could in Arizona, Colorado, and Idaho, and entered the last great timber domain of the north-west. The giant of destruction, who had accounted for seven-eighths of the virgin forest of the United States and paid no attention to Nature's laws which govern regeneration, now made his final assault on the best remaining timber stand of the world. Washington and Oregon are still the lumberman's paradise. Here are the Douglas fir, named after the man who sent the first seeds of them to England. Along a fifty-mile strip between the top of the Cascade Mountains and the Pacific the great trees stand in lordly ranks awaiting their fate. Many of these fine Douglas fir are 10 feet in diameter and tower to a height of 300 feet. When these forests have gone, there will be little left except stands in a few inaccessible regions. The lumberman will have to retrace his steps and be content with small trees of secondary growth which may have sprung up amid the ruins of his making.

For many years, even while all this devastation was taking place, there were earnest conservationists, supported by the Society of American Foresters and the American Forestry Association, who continually strove for legislation which might check the destruction; but it was only after the Forest Service was organized that the Government itself developed the idea of so cutting forests that they would reproduce themselves, removing only the ripe timber, that woodlands might have time to regenerate. It was Theodore Roosevelt who made the first move by sending Gifford Pinchot to India to study the question in the Department of Forests. On his return, Pinchot brought into being the Forestry Service under the Department of Agriculture, and for the first time an attempt was made to regulate felling and apply more conservative methods.

While the lumber magnates were turning the virgin forests

into dollars, the farmers of the Middle West were wheat-growing to satisfy the needs of the population which had sprung up on the wealth of the woods. The Industrial Revolution in England gave rise to a demand for cheap food, and this led to further ploughing of the prairies of the Middle West. Never before in the history of the world had wheat been produced with so little labour; crop after crop was extracted from the deep rich loam of those farmlands, until the soil became exhausted. It was then abandoned for fresh virgin lands to the west. Here was a repetition of the nomadic farmers of Africa, only this time it was on a gigantic scale. Instead of the man with the machete, it was the man with a ploughing outfit; first with his gang plough and six horses, breaking $4\frac{1}{2}$ acres of virgin prairie each day, then with a tractor enormously increasing his speed in exploitation; but always leaving derelict land behind him. It was a rake's progress which spelt inevitable ruin.

Such exploitation of the soil deprives it of its protective covering. Denuded of the trees, scorched by burning, exhausted by overgrazing of the herbage, deprived of its humus by constant cropping without replenishment, the inevitable disaster followed, and the beginnings of a new Sahara were laid. During the dry season the ground surface was reduced to dust and swept along by the wind. Without forest protection, these winds gathered force and played havoc with the denuded lands. When the rain came it was of little value, for the dust could not absorb it, and what remained of the soil with its valuable salts was washed along the gullies to the flooding rivers. It has been estimated that since America was settled an area has been denuded of its surface soil equal to the total area of cultivated land in Germany. At the time of the First World War wheat fetched peak prices, and every available acre of land, whether suitable or not, was ploughed for corn. After the war, when prices dropped, whole farmlands were abandoned, and, being uncultivated, were at the mercy of the elements. Standing one day in Chicago, I was choking with dust, and upon asking my companion the cause of this unpleasant experience, he said: "Oh. that's the Dakotas." This dust was what remained of the top soil of once rich wheat-lands and was blown by the wind for

"Small trees of secondary growth spring up amid the ruins"—sand encroaching on Sitka spruce in Clatsop County.

On the next two pages: Laguna snad-dunes, slowly burying a cedar forest—forming a wonderful "before and after" pair with the picture between pages 24–25.

Another view of Clatsop County—alder and willow-brush being blanketed by heavy sand encroachment.

hundreds of miles, not only causing discomfort in the cities of the east, but baring the rocks from which it came.

Eminent authorities in the U.S.A. have given ominous warnings. A distinguished American engineer some twelve years ago said that with continuance of the manner in which the soil, the mainstay of individual and collective life, is now being squandered, America has left to it less than 100 years of virile national existence. And, if that represents a reasonably accurate statement, it is vastly more significant—if they are to win against the accelerated progression of this gangrenous growth of soil erosion—that they have probably less than twenty years in which to build up the techniques, to recruit the fighting personnel, and, most difficult of all, to change the attitude of millions of people who hold that ownership of land entails the right to maltreat and even to destroy it, regardless of the effect on humanity. This solemn warning was reiterated in 1946 by another American authority, who pointed out that one-eighth of the crop land of the U.S.A. has been ruined by erosion, another eighth nearly ruined, a further quarter has lost more than half its topsoil, and that on a further quarter erosion is already under way. This same authority has predicted that in 100 years from now the United States will not be able to sustain a living man.

This is a drastic statement, and there is evidence that the warnings are being heeded. As far back as 1926 I had the privilege of meeting, among my fellow delegates at the first World Forestry Congress in Rome, representative foresters from the U.S.A. who invited me to visit their country with a view to assisting them to initiate a more progressive and extensive programme of conservation and reafforestation. This I was pleased to do, and at the invitation of Gifford Pinchot I met 200 members of the Society of American Foresters in Washington, D.C. I was granted an audience by President Hoover, who, although at that time he did not see his way clear actively to participate in the cause I had at heart, gave me introductions to the Heads of Departments. I then set out on a nation-wide tour, and, for the better part of two years, devoted myself to preparing a plan. This gave me an opportunity of making a close study of the forestry situation from coast to coast. In every case I had the great advantage of valuable help from foresters, park superintendents, and officials, and was thus able to form a general appraisal.

It was evident that the situation called for immediate action, the rate of timber consumption, including loss by fire and other destructive agencies, being four times as great as the rate of timber growth. The country's requirements amounted to about 25 billion cubic feet each year, while but approximately 6 billion cubic feet was being grown. I recalled that in 1909 the United States produced its entire newsprint supply, but at the time of my survey I found that the country was dependent upon foreign resources for at least two-thirds of it. One Sunday edition of a metropolitan newspaper was using 24 acres of forest a day, while a Chicago paper required 100 acres of Canadian forest every week. The United States, already Canada's biggest customer, was being driven back on Russia for supplies. I saw shipments coming from Archangel in the Baltic up the St. Lawrence and being trans-shipped for Erie in Pennsylvania. To me it seemed a tragedy that this great country should be driven back on Russia for supplies; this country which was already using more wood per head of population than any other country in the world.

During 1932 I travelled 17,000 miles throughout the forest areas of the United States, and visited cut-over areas and witnessed the destruction caused by forest fires. I saw the dreaded scourge, hurricane-driven, death-dealing flames; at times I fought forest fires alongside of foresters, and heard many stories of the destruction of human life and property. It was a fact that the United States was losing by fire every year enough wood to build five-roomed houses for the entire population of a town of 500,000 inhabitants. In California alone $1\frac{1}{2}$ million acres had been burned over. Some years before I was there, one fire in the San Bernardino mountains burned over an area of 15,000 acres and destroyed 3 million feet of timber—yellow pine, sugar pine, cedar, and fir. Before that, in the north-western Minnesota fire, 400 people were burned to death, 2,000 were more or less seriously burned, 13,000 were rendered homeless, and twenty-six towns and villages were partially or completely destroyed. The area covered was 2,000 square miles.

While camping with an old Indian in the redwoods in Northern California, where I had been in search of the finest groves, many of them being threatened by the axe, suddenly over the camp fire one night, almost out of the blue, the old Indian remarked, "Plenty men no get work; there'll be plenty forest fires this summer." He was a man of few words; in fact, for the previous three weeks we had spoken little, most of our intercourse being carried on by signs. This remark therefore caused me to think very deeply. Under the existing régime in those days men were employed at the rate of 5 dollars a day to put out forest fires, casual gangs were taken on, and no sooner was one fire under control than another would spring up, so that such men would have almost continual employment throughout the summer months. Did the old Indian mean to imply that "poor whites" needing employment would set fires going to keep the gangs employed? I remembered that in Canada I had been told that the Forestry Department had abolished payment for casual fire-fighters, and had thereby reduced forest fires by over fifty per cent.

From California I went up through Oregon and Washington and saw the last great forests in these States being exploited. From Washington I crossed the Canadian border into British Columbia, and was distressed to learn from the foresters that they were nearing the end of the virgin Douglas timber. I crossed the Rockies and went up into the Peace River district, where I camped with a Canadian Indian, and after some weeks of careful planning and preparation I set out to find the man who could bring order out of chaos.

Coming from the last fertile country of the west, I met hundreds of distracted farmers from the U.S.A. They had come from the newly-formed Dust Bowl. Many of their farms had been buried by drifting sand, or the topsoil had blown away, making it impossible for them to grow any sort of crop. They had heard of the deep, rich black loam of north-western Alberta, and were moving north to continue their nefarious work of wheat-growing and ultimate destruction. They told me that in many of the worst-hit states nearly all the farmers were getting out. After perhaps three successive crop failures, the farmers could not stand it any longer. I listened to their bitter humour, knowing they were unconscious that they themselves had wrought the destruction and were fleeing from the hell of their own making.

Such meetings and conversations made me feel that my task was all the more imperative, and I pressed on across the Continent back to the east. Everybody was discussing the pending Presidential Election. In New York I met two young friends who were great admirers of Norman Thomas, the Socialist candidate for Presidency. Mrs. Norman Thomas ran a restaurant near Gramercy Park, and there we lunched. After an excellent meal, I drove my young friends down to the Thomas's home on Long Island, where I briefly discussed my plan with Mr. Norman Thomas himself. Almost immediately he said, "Roosevelt is your man; he is going to be the next President. Come and have a swim!" The three of us accompanied him to his swimming-club, and that evening I wired Franklin D. Roosevelt for an appointment.

Driving up through the night from New York, I arrived in Albany about six the next morning, and just before ten o'clock I was awaiting my appointment at Government House. I was greeted warmly by Franklin D. Roosevelt, who exclaimed, "I have been wanting to meet you for a long time." And I replied, "Me, too, you. Do tell me how was it you first became interested in forestry?" "I was staying in your country," he said, "back in 1905, with the Novars in Scotland—Lord Novar was Sir Ronald Munro-Ferguson in those days, and my wife is a kinsman of his. He took me round his woodlands, 20,000 acres, and showed me how he had been able to stem years of agricultural depression by falling back on his woods. He was able to give employment to his dependents in his forests when there was no work for them on the farms." F. D. R. told me that when he got back to New York he sought out Gifford Pinchot, who pulled out of his pocket two pictures: one was of a painting made in China 300 years ago, and the other was a photograph taken of the same site that very year. In the first the hills were completely covered with an evergreen forest. At the base of the hill there was a populous city, settled in a fertile valley with a river running through it. The only indication of logging to be seen in the painting was a little water chute with some logs coming down the slipway. The photograph taken 300 years later showed the same contour of the hills, but they were bleak and bare. Not a vestige of their former glory remained. The one-time fertile valley was strewn with great boulders, the cover gone, and the dried-up soil with its fertility lost for ever. All that remained of that flourishing city was a few derelict huts. Roosevelt said that that had made such an impression on him that he asked Gifford Pinchot to come and talk to the business men of New York. He said, "From that time I have never looked back. You know what I have done by way of planting on my own place at Hyde Park, and you know what I have done for the State of New York." I said, "Yes, indeed. I know that here you have planted sixty per cent of all the trees planted this year in the whole of the States and now you are going to do for the whole country what you have done in the State of New York." He looked straight at me and said, "What do you mean?" I replied, "But you are going to be the next President." "What makes you think that?" he retorted. "Well," said I, "I have just done 17,000 miles in your country, preparing a forestry plan, and don't you think an outsider often has a better perspective than the man on the spot? Besides, yesterday I was discussing my plan with Norman Thomas, and he said 'Roosevelt is your man; he's going to be next President.' " "Did he say that?" "Yes, he believes you will be able to bring relief to millions of unemployed as he would like to have done if he had a ghost of a chance of the presidency. Do you know you can give immediate and direct employment to 250,000 young men in forestry?" And his quick reply was: "Couldn't you make it 300,000?" I told him how I had just been visiting my old University of Saskatchewan and inspecting the agricultural station at Southerland, where ever since my student days they had been experimenting with the most suitable trees for shelter-belts, and how I wished that every farmer, instead of planting a wind-belt around his home, would plant a belt of trees around his farm. We discussed the truly alarming problem of unemployment: there were already 18 million unemployed, and it appeared that the figures were mounting by mathematical progression; it had been calculated that before long in the United States there would be over 30 million

workless and penniless. I told him of my sojourn in the redwoods and what the old Indian had said about unemployment
and forest fires, and how in Canada as soon as they stopped
paying casual labour for fire-fighting they reduced forest fires
by fifty per cent. At that moment, like a flash, Roosevelt caught
the idea which later brought the Civilian Conservation Corps
into being.

Chapter Seven

RECLAMATION

*The fundamental idea of forestry is the perpetuation of forests
by use. Forest protection is not an end of itself; it is a means
to increase and sustain the resources of our country and the industries which depend upon them.*

Theodore Roosevelt.

WHEN FRANKLIN D. ROOSEVELT BECAME PRESIDENT OF THE
United States of America in March, 1933, he assumed
office with the country apparently heading for disaster.
The theme of his acceptance speech in Chicago was: "Back to
the land with forestry—without vision a people perish."

On my return to England after the Ottawa Conference,
where I had read a paper on the world forestry situation, I
busied myself with the preparation of plans for employing
some thousands from the distressed areas of Britain, but failed
to find another Roosevelt. On hearing the result of the Presidential Election, I cabled my congratulations to F. D. R.,
and by return post I received a charming letter from him from
Warm Springs, which prompted me to take the next boat out.
On my arrival in the States, I conferred with Henry Morgenthau, Jnr. I met him in New York. At that time he was Chairman of the Farms Board of that State, and he was Governor
Roosevelt's right-hand man in the valuable task of bringing
the marginal lands back within the scope of forestry. These
areas once had borne pine forests, and after the trees had been
swept away attempts had been made to farm them, but with
very disappointing results. Considerable success had been
achieved by Roosevelt and Morgenthau, with the result that
out of 100,000 acres of planting throughout America during
that year, 60,000 acres had been planted in the State of New
York.

While I was with Henry Morgenthau I recalled briefly my
audience with the President in Albany, and said: "What you
and the President have done for the State of New York you can

do for the whole country. You can plant trees and grow gold for the nation, and by so doing can serve the land, assist agriculture, and help to stem the oncoming timber famine." I pointed out that it was on the strength of my report that the largest afforestation corporation in the world had been launched. I presented him with figures which he immediately questioned, raising objections on many accounts, although I instinctively felt that he was already on my side, but wanted to be further convinced and equipped for the great task which was awaiting him. In this thinking, hard-headed man of affairs I felt the emotion of the ideal, and, although his head was in the clouds of altruism with the thought that the plan before him was going to bring fresh hope to many thousands of unemployed, yet his feet were on a very solid foundation—the earth of economics. I had to prove to him the economic aspect of the project which I laid before him. His masterly mind was forever turning my vision of growing trees into financial returns; but whereas I thought in millions of acres, he thought and spoke in billions of dollars. Quickly he grasped the significance of my figures— figures laboriously collected over many years of practical experience in many lands. He swiftly absorbed them and, instead of crabbing the scheme, wanted to make it even bigger.

He had been a patient listener, but he could also be a most convincing talker. Having absorbed the project, in his mind the idea quickly evolved into a nation-wide scheme. The child of my idea had grown into a giant before my very eyes. Working in close collaboration with Morgenthau, the first measure Roosevelt arranged when he was installed at the White House was for the equivalent of £100,000,000 to be available for work relief. The second was to establish the Civilian Conservation Corps.

On March 22, 1933, Robert Fechner received a long-distance call from the White House requesting his immediate presence in Washington. That very evening a Bill had been sent to Congress by the President, proposing the setting up of a vast army as a measure partially to relieve unemployment and, at the same time, to accomplish useful work. Congress enacted the legislation, and the President signed the Bill on March 31.

Burned-over area after logging, Oregon.

All that is left of a once-happy forest home.

One Sunday edition . . .

On April 5 Robert Fechner was appointed Director of the Civilian Conservation Corps. The next day the President sent for him and asked him how long it would take to get the first conservation camp going. The Director thought it would take some time, but the President said, "I want the first camp going in three weeks' time." And it was.

I was glad to be able to spend the first few months of this great President's term of office in the States, where I was able to watch and confer with those who were responsible for bringing the new camps into being. I saw the young men in action and joined them over the camp fires at night, when I would tell them of my own experiences as a forester. I also gave many broadcast talks in support of conservation.

The creation of the Civilian Conservation Corps was a stupendous task, but the genius of the President inspired the co-operation of the four departments—War, Interior, Agriculture, and Labour—whose united efforts achieved unprecedented success. Under the competent supervision of trained foresters and technicians of Federal and State departments and agencies dealing with conservation matters, some 250,000 young men, with a sprinkling of more experienced war veterans and Indians, were soon forming camps and carrying out valuable work. These lads were before long planting new forests with the little trees of their raising, they were strengthening forest and park protection systems to reduce forest devastation by fires, insects, and disease, and thinning cut-over areas to make woodlands more productive. By the second year there were 300,000 men working in the Civilian Conservation Corps, and by the fifth year there were 4,500 camps, of 200 men each, operating in State and private forests. As many as 300,000 men a day would set out from their camps to plant trees, build trails, erect fire-protection towers, lay telephone lines, and improve grazing conditions in national forests and in public domains. On the deserted farmlands they were able to carry out valuable work of reclamation and rehabilitation. They drained ditches, built check-dams, and planted quick-growing trees and vegetation to protect farmlands from soil wastage, to conserve water and prevent floods. They conducted campaigns against the deadly white pine blister rust,

E

the gipsy moth, bark beetles, and rodents. They improved conditions for wild life, and did a host of other jobs related to the national task of conserving and rebuilding America's natural resources.

Those who have not experienced life in the wilds have little idea of the hardships to be endured by these new recruits. Floods and forest fires exact their toll of human life. Even in the ordinary activities of everyday work there are frequent opportunities calling for quick decisions that may save a pal from injury or death. In fighting forest fires, the young men of the C.C.C. performed a service of the highest order. And, as an example, several hundreds of these gallant lads will never forget their terrible experience in the Blackwater Canyon, where the worst fire for over a quarter of a century took toll of one human life with every 1,000 acres of timber destroyed. The most spectacular work accomplished by the C.C.C. was in this field of forest-fire prevention. Before they had been operating very long, they reduced forest fires by seventy-five per cent. They cut thousands of miles of trails for the purpose of fire control, they cleaned up cut and burnt-over areas and thus reduced the fire risk. Hundreds of look-out towers were built and manned by trained observers. They prepared proper camping sites for tourists who followed their trails, and, by building stone fire-hearths, the risk of a forest fire through carelessness was greatly reduced.

Next in importance comes land reclamation, before soil-erosion-prevention operations have been completed on a nation-wide scale. It was a noble conception of the President to plant a wall of millions of trees down the centre of the United States, consisting of wind-breaks extending 1,000 miles long, from the Canadian border down to the Panhandle of Texas. It consisted of a series of belts, 100 miles wide, comprised of drought-resisting species. This backbone of trees was intended to check the wind which for years had carried away the soil of the farmlands, and also to serve as a trap for moisture. The trees planted were suited to the climate, and the shrubs on the outside rows acted as wind-breaks. Even among the experts there were many who prophesied failure; but, in spite of adverse conditions, the entire appearance of the countryside is now being changed. Little trees that were planted in shifting sands in 1934 have attained a height of 40 or 50 feet. The shelter-belt strips have transformed the sandy desert and have broken the flat monotony of the plains. Helpful birds are once more returning, and the farmers are again able to plant under the protection of the sheltering trees.

Not all trees will grow on the prairie, with its low rainfall, severe winter, and hot summer. It has been the task of foresters through long years of research and experiment to determine which trees and shrubs are best fitted for the ceaseless battle with the prairie winds and droughts. Among the trees which were found to be best suited for shelter-belt planting in the Great Plains area are the cottonwood poplar, green ash, Chinese elm, bur oak, hackberry, honey locust, and, less extensively, willows. Shrubs chiefly used include lilac, wild plum, and Russian olive. In the Dakotas and Nebraska, the principal shrub used is the caragana, with some chokecherry. Farther south, from Nebraska to Texas, the black locust (or false acacia) has been found an excellent tree for shelter-belts and is widely used. This is one of the best trees for increasing the fertility of the soil; it is leguminous and injects nitrogen into the earth. Phenomenal crops have been grown near its roots. Other valuable trees used in the south are the apricot, black walnut, catalpa or Indian bean, Russian mulberry, osage-orange, and the pecan nut. The desert willow has been found a satisfactory shrub in Oklahoma and Texas.

From the nurseries of the Prairie States Forestry Project come the trees for the great planting programme. The majority of these nurseries are leased from local professional nurserymen.

The foresters make a point of collecting as much seed as they can locally, for it has been found by experience that seed from a distance does not produce trees fit to cope with the severe conditions with which the young trees have to contend.

Here and there are pioneers possessed of initiative and vision who have set the example which others now may follow. One of the most outstanding of these is J. J. Lydick, of Craig, Nebraska, who nearly thirty years ago started planting shelter-belts on his farm of 240 acres. It was two miles from the loess hills, which with the bluffs and flats extend twenty miles from the Missouri River. It was open land devoid of trees. The average annual precipitation was 28 inches, though at times it was as low as fifteen. The water table was over 60 feet below the surface. It was a land of wind and dust, with wide extremes of temperature.

The story of his planting has been told by M. B. Jenkins in *American Forests*, the journal of the American Forestry Association. He tells how, soon after Lydick started to farm, hay-fever so reduced his vitality that his doctor said he must go to the mountains, where he could breathe the scent of the pine, spruce, and fir and thus escape the dust-laden atmosphere of the plains. But this young man was in love with farming and was loath to leave his land. He decided that, if it was the scent of the pines and the spruce and the fir that he needed, he would plant them there on his own place. He started collecting seed and raising young trees in nursery beds. He chose Colorado spruce, Douglas fir, Austrian and ponderosa pine, and Norway poplar, and he arranged them with slower-growing trees on the outside and the evergreens forming an impenetrable barrier against wind and storm. He transplanted them two or three times in nursery lines, so that they might become well rooted before being planted out into their final stations. He took pains to cultivate the ground within the belt that he planted. However busy he was, he always gave the trees his first attention. His neighbours ridiculed him for his pains and for wasting so much valuable land growing trees. "It will never pay," they told him, and yet to-day, thirty years afterwards, there are many of his old neighbours who would like to exchange farms with him.

Lydick proved that permanent, well-arranged farm plantings and crop shelter-belts are as much of an asset as barns or ploughs. They are as essential to agriculture as modern factories are to industry. The hardiness and present vigour of the trees on that Nebraska farm speak well for the wise selection of seed and choice of species. Even during the drought years of 1934 and 1936, not a single conifer was lost, although the precipitation fell to 15 inches. Within the zone of protection from these living green walls, the average farm crops were more than double those which grow on the outside. In the drought year of

1934, potatoes yielded 200 bushels to the acre, while other potato fields in the same county dried out. That year not a single bushel of potatoes was grown within a radius of ten miles of that tree-surrounded farm. The corn-fields were not irrigated, but the yield was from 35 to 40 bushels to the acre, while neighbouring fields without the benefit of shelter-belts were burned up by hot winds. The orchards were an inspiring sight. Apple trees were loaded to breaking point with fruit of good size and quality, and close by were large patches of heavy-yielding raspberries.

When Mr. Lydick was asked how he accounted for such heavy yields, he said that he attributed it to the fact that the winter snows melted where they fell instead of being driven into drifts miles away, as is often the case. The protection provided by the trees reduced the force of summer winds, so that they caused little loss of soil moisture; nor had they carried away the valuable light humus particles of the upper soil. This pioneer had found that he did not need much rain to grow crops so long as he kept the soil light and friable. It is interesting to note that Mr. Lydick never irrigated his trees, but depended entirely on cultivation, and this only for the first three or four years. Yet he has produced specimen trees and symmetrical wind-breaks such as cannot be equalled anywhere else in Nebraska or the United States. This planter of trees has rendered a valuable service by demonstrating how shelter-belts conserve soil moisture and increase the productiveness of the land. What is more, after thirty years he has completely regained his health and now lives to enjoy the fruits of his labour.

Such work is an example of farm forestry such as was advocated by Nebraska's apostle of planting, J. Stirling Morton, the author and founder of Arbor Day, who continually urged settlers to plant a portion of their grasslands to trees. He assured them the trees would control wind and water erosion, afford comfort and better living conditions, and provide future wood supplies. He foresaw the time when the roads and highways from the Missouri River to the Rocky Mountains would be lined with coniferous and hardwood trees.

It was through the influence of J. Stirling Morton that the

American Forestry Association, at a meeting in Omaha, Nebraska, in September, 1898, passed the following resolution:

"Whereas this Association believes a proper series of wind-breaks would so regulate the surface air currents as materially to reduce evaporation, thereby conserving a precipitation that under those conditions would be ample for grain husbandry; THEREFORE BE IT RESOLVED BY THIS ASSOCIATION that our National Congress should create a commission for the purpose of investigating the feasibility of establishing forest wind-breaks on the plains of New Mexico, Texas, Colorado, Kansas, Wyoming, Nebraska, and the two Dakotas."

It would appear that no action was taken at the time, but this is an historic document which is significant of the plans and purposes of a forward-looking group of forestry pioneers. Although much planting was done by some individual farmers, many failed, for they had not arrived at the knowledge of the best technique. Tree survival depends on choice of species, source of seed, and the provision of adequate cultivation during he early years of planting. Wherever farmers have succeeded with their trees they have generally become successful with their farm crops. The combined experience of the pioneer planters indicate that farm forestry is an important factor in the solution of food production and ultimate human survival.

The American people have now accepted this reclamation by tree-planting as a vital part of their future programme. The foresters working on this project picture an environment where man and beast will obtain cover from the fury of the elements. The launching of the C.C.C. inaugurated a nation-wide war of reconstruction—not a war of destruction. It was waged to build up America's human and natural resources. That struggle was fought on two fronts. On the one hand, President Roosevelt, through the C.C.C. camps, was able to save an army of idle youth from the moral erosion caused by unemployment, while, on the other, he attempted to save his land from deterioration and barrenness. The President appealed to their imagination. Were they not the sons and the grandsons of Americans who had conquered the West, always moving that frontier farther and farther back? By launching the C.C.C., he created a new frontier for them, and hundreds of thousands of these young men, who would otherwise have had little or nothing to do, were sent to outdoor camps in the forests and parks, where they were given jobs—re-creative jobs in the fullest sense of the word. They were taught self-discipline, not military training. This army in turn co-operated with Nature in helping to restore the green glory to the hills, and fertility to the valleys and plains.

Chapter Eight

THE BALANCE OF NATURE

Help Nature and work on with her; and Nature will regard thee as one of her creators and make obeisance. And she will open wide before thee the portals of her secret chambers, lay bare before thy gaze the treasures hidden in the very depths of her virgin bosom.

The Voice of the Silence.

EARTH'S GREEN COVERING IS THE BASIS OF LIFE, WHETHER human or animal. Vegetation constitutes the foundation of our energy and the very source of all life, for in the final analysis this applies even to carnivorous animals. The only difference is that the carnivores obtain the natural energies stored in plants second-hand, while the vegetarian animals receive them directly. Man also, whether he eats vegetables and fruit or animals, draws his vitality from the same vegetable world, which in turn springs from the soil.

Trees are the highest example of the vegetable kingdom. Unlike human beings or animals, they function in every sphere. Their roots are in the lithosphere and are always in contact with the hydrosphere through the circulation of water in the earth, their trunks and branches are in the atmosphere, and their foliage receives radiation from the stratosphere. The foliage also receives other cosmic rays falling on our planet and is in contact with atmospheric vapour and moisture, which comes to it in the form of rain. Throughout the whole of its growing period the work of a tree is incessant. Its thousands of leaves constantly evaporate and breathe out water into the atmosphere, while the whole surface of the leaves is continually absorbing the maximum quantity of solar energy. The leaves also take in nitrogen from the atmosphere and various other elements and radiations, which they accumulate and elaborate by means of their millions of chlorophyll cells. No other living thing draws into itself vitality from such universal sources;

A 20-acre field completely enclosed by wind-breaks, Nebraska.

Terraced-strip cultivation, with terrace orchards in contour and wind-breaks.

Ploughing-under green manure.

CONTOU

The ground prepared.

One-year-old trees planted.

LTIVATION

The same trees at six years old.

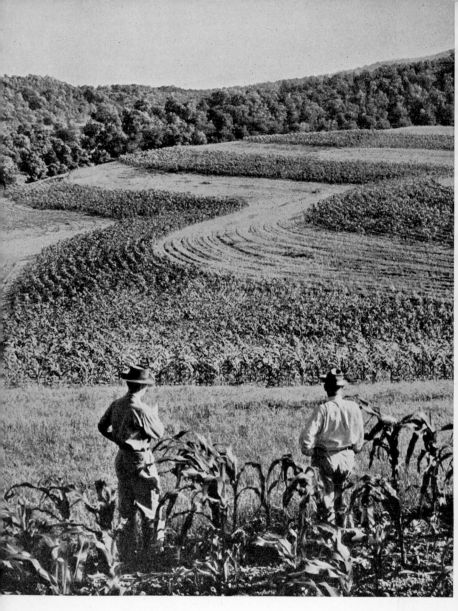

The finished shelter-belt.

therefore trees make the greatest contribution to physical life on this planet.

Despite the fact that his very existence is dependent upon them, man has abused this greatest gift and through his folly has sadly upset the balance of Nature.

Primitive man lived by the forest, but when new desires were created he cleared it, thus removing the source of his natural food, and started his artificial way of life. His new habits were contagious and spread with ever-increasing momentum round the earth, until to-day few regions are to be found where Nature reigns. Some virgin forests may still be found in the North and South Americas, along the Pacific Coast, in some islands of the Pacific, and in Russia. But in the greater part of the world the forests have been removed or invaded and their soil depleted.

Resulting from unnatural industries, from war and greed, the modern world has reached such a degree of mechanism that the soil of one part of the earth is transported to another to feed those who make no contribution themselves to its fertility. In the early days of World War II, people were shocked at the reports that the Germans were sending train-loads of good black earth from Czechoslovakian forests each day into Germany to reinforce the worked-out lands of their own country. But little do the public realize that this process has been going on throughout the world for the past century. For instance, when the early settlers found themselves in the newly discovered continent of Australia, they took to sheep-farming and wheat-growing because they could make big money from these. Their flocks grazed on virgin lands and they felled the forest to extend their farms. They exported their wheat and wool harvests to other lands and with them their land's fertility. As the market boomed their flocks and farms increased, and soon the sparse covering of grass was overgrazed and the thin layer of topsoil worn away—exported in the form of wheat, wool, and mutton.

It took rather longer for the United States of America and Canada to export the fertility of the Middle West. For the greater part they had deep, rich black loam which they could plough for miles without meeting any obstruction. Other areas were cleared of the forest and planted to corn, and this in turn was exported. Nothing was returned to the soil. Year after year these pioneers gnawed into their deep, rich black loam which had been built up by Nature through the centuries, and sent it across the oceans in return for gold. That gold would not return the humus to their land nor help them to play fair to the earth. The gold received by those who sold their soil was but a mere pittance by comparison with the cost of rehabilitating their land.

The taking of food from the topsoil and failing to return it in compost is suicidal. Western man has been undermining his very existence since the introduction of chemical manures and water sanitation. He has been raping the earth, taking from it crops of every kind, and has failed to recognize the law of return and fair play. Few people realize that every ton of wheat grain represents four-fifths of a ton of earth. Vast quantities of topsoil are, as it were, moved in ships from one country to another. Where does this go? Surely some country must be benefiting from such imports. In so far as this produce is fed to livestock, it may be returned to the land as farmyard manure; but the great majority of food consumed by city dwellers eventually leaves their bodies in the form of solid and liquid waste and is lost to the land owing to modern sewage.

Addressing the first Men of the Trees Summer School at Oxford in 1938, Sir Albert Howard, C.I.E., M.A., in his paper on "The Floor of the Forest", said: "In the forest the processes of decay and the processes of growth always balance one another. The vegetable waste, together with the by-products of the large animal population which every piece of woodland maintains, form an intimate mixture on the floor of the forest. . . . In dealing with its own wastes, the forest creates none of the problems with which mankind in similar circumstances is constantly struggling—smells, flies, dustbins, infectious diseases, the disposal of water-borne sewage, town and other councils, an army of officials, more and more rates, and a growing burden of debt. The forest is the perfect sanitarian, the supreme chemist and economist. . . ."

And again, in his recent book, *The Maintenance of Soil Fertility in Great Britain*, Sir Albert draws attention to one of the most destructive stupidities of pseudo-science which for 300 years has been ruining the fertility of the whole British Empire. He says: "By far the most important demand of the Industrial Revolution was the creation of two new hungers—the hunger of a rapidly increasing urban population and the hunger of its machines. Both needed the things raised on the land: both have seriously depleted the reserves of fertility in our soils. Neither of these hungers has been accompanied by the return of the respective wastes to the land. Instead, vast sums of money were spent in completely side-tracking these wastes and preventing their return to the land which so sorely needed them. Much ingenuity was devoted to developing an effective method of removing the human wastes to the rivers and seas. These finally took the shape of our present water-borne sewage system. The contents of the dustbins of house and factory first found their way into huge dumps, and then into incinerators or into refuse tips sealed by a thin covering of cinders or soil." If all the humus formed from waste matter from millions of cases of oranges and apples, millions of tons of beef and mutton, wheat and oil, were used, how fertile would the land be. Britain has been notorious for waste and improvidence, and the famine conditions with which she is now confronted are the result of ignorance and wastefulness.

It behoves us as the fortunate dwellers in these islands, and as the greatest food-importers in the world, to reverse the process and set an example in conservation.

The Men of the Trees, after twenty-five years of endeavour, are at length beginning to discern a change in the attitude of the general public. There is a growing appreciation of trees, not only for their beauty, but for the vital contribution that they make to life. Outstanding among the new voices is an English farmer who is making an appeal for more enlightenment among farmers throughout the world, asking them for a more generous treatment of the tree, which can render such a great service to agriculture.

The productive capacity of the soil depends on trees, and agriculture is dependent on forestry: the one devoted to the planting, conservation, and harvesting of trees, and the other to grains, fruits, vegetables, and animals. Fish, game, and honey may be considered as secondary forest crops. The honey bee is one of the greatest gifts to the farm and forest, for not only does it fertilize the farm crops, but also the flowers of trees.

Every farm contains land that will not produce farm crops but no land is of such poor quality that it will not support tree growth. If the farmer will only recognize the value of the trees to himself and the importance of the forest to the country and to mankind in general, he will undertake to grow crops of trees with as much care and forethought as he spends on producing other crops. Forestry and agriculture are complementary and may be practised on the same farm. The forest provides fuel and construction timber, fence posts, and wood for implements, and, while growing, the trees provide shelter for stock and nesting places for helpful birds that destroy harmful insects. Forestry, too, helps in the economy of the farm by providing employment in the winter, thus enabling a farmer to maintain a larger permanent staff of farm-forest workers throughout the year.

Above all, forests increase the fertility of the land. It is possible by planting unproductive areas or the lower grades of farmland to improve their quality. With the exception of steep hillsides or sand, all land can be brought within the range of agriculture through the improvement of the soil made possible by the leaf fall and irrigation of forest trees. It is therefore evident that the economy of forestry and that of agriculture are intimately connected. So close is this integration that when a farmer suddenly sells his entire wood crop and removes his hedgerow timber, a severe threat is made upon the economy of the farm. To fell all the trees on a property is often a prelude to disaster. In many parts of the world, farm abandonment and the decline of agriculture have coincided with forest destruction.

The objection often raised to tree-planting is that one has to wait too long to reap the harvest, whereas the farmer is able to produce an annual crop and thus have an annual income. The forester, on the other hand, may have to wait the whole of his life before his harvest is ripe. This, indeed, is a strong argument in favour of farmers practising forestry. On considering the question more closely, however, there are short-rotation tree crops, such as willows for basket-making, which, when once established, can be harvested every year. Cricket-bat willows have been found to be a profitable investment, yielding returns in ten or twelve years. There are also fast-growing species of poplar which are now being planted in several parts of the world, where they will bring returns in from twenty to thirty years, and, while growing, yield valuable sets each year which can be disposed of for cash or used to extend the farm plantation. In the case of many tree crops, there are incidental products during the growth of the wood crop: for instance, syrup and sugar from maple, various gums and resins—such as turpentine and rosin—cones, faggots, berries, wild honey, fruit, nuts, fish, and game. Unlike farm crops, the forest provides its own fertilizer through the annual fall of its leaves, bark, and twigs. Inorganic fertilizers are never applied, nor are poison-sprays needed; in fact, the forest is self-supporting and is a complete biological unit.

The home woods on a farm can maintain that balance of Nature so essential to productivity and the well-being of man and beast. A forest or wood is not merely an aggregation of trees, but a living community. The interrelation and interdependence between man, plants, fungi, animals, birds, and insects are countless, yet they are often overlooked in farming and forestry plans. No farm is complete without its balanced home wood, where so many good influences are at work. No forest or home wood can contribute its best unless it contains a mixture of species, both broad-leaved and coniferous trees. Pure stands of conifers tend to make the ground acid and fail to provide litter with soil-improving properties. This may be accounted for by the fact that the micro-fauna of the soil is poorer under pines than under mixed hardwoods, and the number of earthworms is less and their weight but a third of those found in the soil of the natural woods. Moreover, pine woods are inhospitable to birds and wild life. Lacking browse, deer are liable to bark the trees, and squirrels and grouse destroy the buds. When a pure coniferous forest is artificially created, the balance of Nature is disturbed. Birds may forsake the area owing to absence of food, and thus permit insect pests to establish themselves unmolested. Insectivorous birds are the

friends of both the farmer and the forester, and are well known
to be important controls of farm and forest insects.

As among human beings, so with trees, prevention is better
than cure. If we are to avoid the disastrous outbreaks which
have ravaged Continental forests, we must adopt a long-sighted,
comprehensive, and permanent policy which will control the
injurious fauna and prevent their ever becoming pests.

Protection may be natural and indirect, or artificial and
direct. The first can be achieved by good silviculture, by providing conditions for the most favourable growth and at the
same time producing an unfavourable state for the development of the parasite and plunderer. The best way, if not the
only way, to achieve this is by careful and correct choice of
species, composition, or mixtures, method of regeneration and
after-treatment. The silvicultural method is most successful
against physical damage by windfall, fire, frost, or snow, but
only partially effective against fungi and insects, and of less
use in practice against injurious birds and animals. These must
be dealt with by biological control—that is to say, by the active
encouragement of beneficial agents and the suppression of their
enemies. The encouragement of useful insects or the introduction of parasites on harmful ones is difficult and sometimes
dangerous, because the balance of Nature is so fine in adjustment that it can easily be upset. There is a classical instance of
this in the case of the Kootenay scale on oranges. The growers
in California had heard of the success of the Australian ladybirds, and imported a quantity into their groves with great
success. The Florida growers thought they would do likewise,
and ordered a supply of these same ladybirds from California,
which duly arrived with sufficient scale to keep them happy in
transit. The remainder of this, together with the ladybirds,
was turned loose in the groves of Florida. In a very short time
the Florida growers observed a new kind of scale which quickly
spread throughout the country, causing a vast amount of
damage, while their original pest did not prove to be the right
food for that particular kind of ladybird. The reduction of the
new pest took them several years, at the cost of millions of
dollars.

Another instance of failure of the biological method nearer

home was when stoats were sent from Norfolk to Australia, with a view to reducing the ravages of rabbits in that country. Very soon Norfolk became overrun with rabbits, and to this day they are still increasing. As in many other parts of the country, they are proving to be one of the most injurious pests known to the farmer and forester, and costing the country something in the neighbourhood of 70 millions a year.

The encouragement of predacious birds for the control of harmful insects is easier than that of useful insects, and is something that everyone can help with. It should be remembered that there are two factors only which govern the decrease of any organism—lack of food and the presence of enemies. Insects and animals can be controlled biologically by means of other insects and parasitic fungi. All parasites are characterized by their almost complete interdependence on one species or genus of insect. They can control their numbers, but not annihilate them; they are the police rather than the military force in Nature. Moreover, from their mode of life it is readily understood that parasites cannot by themselves check any sudden increase of injurious insects, for their generation is always one stage, usually one year, behind that of their hosts. Parasitic insects must be regarded as an ever-present and necessary form of natural control, which it is only possible to encourage by the discouragement of its enemies.

In England the starling is one of the most useful birds all the year round, but especially in summer.

Collinge gives as its adult food: injurious insects 26·5 per cent, beneficial insects 2·5 per cent; nestlings: ground beetles 7·2 per cent, Mellonthinae 13·5 per cent, various weevils 3·7 per cent, lepidopterous larvae 39·3 per cent, and as the fledgling period is about twenty days and the young are visited from 250 to 350 times a day, the number of injurious insects consumed is very great. The results from the judicious use of nesting-boxes on the Continent have been so successful that in all well-managed woods where natural sites are probably very limited, a great deal can be accomplished by providing suitable nesting-boxes. I have no fault to find with the starling, except that he will often sit or swing on the leading shoot of a Sitka spruce until it breaks or is seriously injured.

The redstart is a beneficial bird of considerable importance, since it is readily encouraged to nest in artificial sites. The robin can also be encouraged by the provision of suitable nesting-boxes. It is common in woods, where it feeds almost entirely on insects obtained from the ground and foliage. Other closely allied species are the blackcap, grasshopper-warbler, garden-warbler, and nightingale.

The arboreal warblers form a very valuable check on the numbers of small defoliatory larvae and to a less extent of Rhyncophoia. These warblers feed largely on the adult and egg stages, and so their utility is increased. The blue tit, unfortunately, is almost restricted to broad-leaved trees and is of primary importance, specially with Rhynchota, particularly the "woolly" chermes, the felted beech coccus, and the ash and willow scale. The coal tit is a true forest species, and because of its other characteristics is the most useful member of the genus. It is seen searching the trunks of trees, and also comes to the ground to search for pupae concealed in the grass. The marsh tit, although less useful, is distinctly beneficial. The willow tit is of great importance because of its preference for Coleoptera and the small bud and needle infesting Lepidoptera. The long-tailed tit is of restricted utility on account of its habitat, but of primary importance, specially, when it wanders in winter. The goldcrest, which inhabits all kinds of coniferous woods, particularly of spruce and Douglas fir, but not young plantations, is entirely arboreal and lives principally on insects and spiders obtained from twigs and needles. The great tit's usefulness is due to its constant search for Rhynchota, which are its staple food, and it feeds on them throughout the winter. These birds must destroy enormous numbers of Chermesidae. To encourage them in woods devoid of unsound timber, nesting-boxes must be provided by the middle of March to induce most tits to nest. Their enemy, the sparrowhawk, should be destroyed.

The woodpeckers are often accused of damaging trees, but evidence shows that they rarely, if ever, attack or disfigure healthy timber. The cuckoo is of great value to forestry. Unlike other birds, they are not forced to remain in particular areas for nesting purposes, and are therefore free to move about wherever

SARAH YUSTER
165 Corson Ave.
Staten Island, N.Y. 10301
(718) 448-2132

ELIZABETH SHEPPARD YUSTER 1985
  Oil On Canvas 34" X 42"

SARAH YUSTER

165 Corson Ave.
Staten Island, N.Y. 10301
(718) 448-2132

Aerial view of contour-planted orchard.

Gully scalped and planted.

The same gully after five years.

food is most abundant. They search all types of vegetation for larval forms, and it has been estimated that 100 cuckoos in fifteen days can account for over $2\frac{1}{2}$ million Scolytidae of the Coleoptera family. The nightjar is of first importance, particularly on newly-reclaimed areas where cockchafer and bark-beetle pests are likely to be severe. Gamekeepers frequently shoot the nightjar in mistake for a hawk.

Owls are good foresters. The long-eared owl destroys rats, mice, voles, and small rabbits. The tawny owl, found in broad-leaved woods, feeds on long-tailed mice, shrews, grass mice, water-voles, and rabbits. It is one of the most useful birds in the British Isles. The barn owl and the little owl are of less importance and sometimes destroy other useful birds.

It is important to appreciate the value of the systematic, as opposed to chance, methods of forest protection. Continental foresters have learned by bitter experience the result of the neglect of biological control in their artificial plantations and woodlands. We must not fall into the same errors, but learn from their mistakes. It seems that we are taking no more precautions than the German foresters did seventy or eighty years ago. The fact that till now we have suffered little tends to make us serenely content. The importance of action now has been heightened by the extensive felling of timber. Often lop and top and unwanted trees have been left in the woods, dead and dying timber has been untouched, while the best has been taken. Unless precautionary measures are adopted, the country may be swept with pests, causing the destruction and disappearance of the few woodlands and plantations that remain.

The biological control of enemies by predatory birds and animals may be of limited practical application. It is thoroughly economic, however, to take steps to encourage the natural enemies of voles and mice, for, like insects, it is important to exclude the animals from the forest. They are so small and subject to such prodigious increase that artificial control is out of the question. The cost of artificial control is many times that of silvicultural and biological control. Continental experience shows costly failures. In Bavaria in one year alone the expense of artificial protection, leaving out of account the loss of timber involved, was estimated at £100,000.

F

In America whole tree species have been swept from the woods by diseases, even though large sums of money were spent on artificial measures in an attempt to control or eradicate. It has been said that if all the birds were removed from any country, in two years' time it would be impossible to grow any farm crop, despite the many chemical insecticides of these modern days. The good forester will place nesting-boxes to attract helpful birds, and farmers will do well to plant and protect hedgerow timber to provide nesting-places for their feathered friends.

Birds are great distributors of tree seeds, especially those with fleshy fruits; jays have been known to plant acorns.

There have been cases where birds have exerted injurious influences upon forests, but this is usually where the natural balance has been disturbed by man. I have observed a case where almost the entire crop of seeds of a pine forest was destroyed by blackbirds and other birds. They preferred to take the seed from burned areas where it was exposed on the soil. Large birds, such as pigeons, may break the leading shoots of trees, especially those of the tallest trees in a plantation which serve them as look-outs. The concentration of starlings or sparrows continually roosting in trees may be injurious to their growth. Birds have been known to distribute forest pests, such as the seeds of ribes, the intermediate host of the white pine blister, but on the whole the good that birds do far outweighs the harm.

Squirrels, by eating the bark round white pine blister rust cankers, may reduce the volume of spores infecting the ribes host plants. Rodents are notorious seed-eaters, but at the same time they do help to distribute seed. I have seen a beech hedge along the bottom of a bank entirely planted by squirrels. They had stored the mast and forgotten to eat it.

Harmful fungi are better known than their helpful relations. Some of the helpful ones provide, as it were, a "living bridge" for conducting the nutriment in the soil through their cellular threads to the feeding rootlets of the plant or tree. These symbiotic fungi are formed in humus by the great majority of our farm plants and forest trees. These are known as mycorrhiza-formers. If a healthy young pine or oak is lifted from the soil, a white fungus in the form of threads will be observed, attached to the hair roots of the little tree. At first sight it looks as though the tree has been attacked by root-fungus, while in fact this particular fungus is fulfilling a most useful purpose. Indeed, young trees, whether oak, beech, larch, pine, or spruce, would not thrive without the help of this useful fungoid growth, for it helps to prepare the plant food and bring it into a condition in which it can better be assimilated through the feeding roots of the plant or tree. The presence of toadstools in the woods is an outward and visible sign that the mycorrhiza is at work. Nature has provided the roots of forest trees with a very remarkable organization. In the absence of humus there is no mycorrhiza, growth is stunted and often diseased; but where natural conditions prevail, abundant mycorrhiza ensures the fertility of the soil.

The human body is the earth in miniature. For is it not true that each part of the body is dependent on the other? If any part becomes defective or is lost, the whole balance is upset. And so it is with the earth. For millions of years the earth has built up and maintained its unique routine, which is now threatened. Let man go forward in partnership with Nature and use his accumulated knowledge to foster and maintain this essential balance.

Chapter Nine

FORESTRY IN RUSSIA

The world will not be a good place for any of us to live in unless we make it a good place for all of us to live in.

THE SOVIET UNION HAS THE RESPONSIBILITY OF THE LARGEST forest area in the world. About thirty-eight per cent of the total land surface is classed as forest. It is to her credit that Russia started on a conservative forest policy long before any apparent necessity arose. While other countries were squandering their woodland wealth, this nation was maintaining its forest capital and at the same time becoming one of the largest timber exporters in the world. For many years Leningrad and Archangel have been renowned for the high quality of the timber that has passed through their ports, and Leningrad has now been made one of the most efficient and up-to-date ports for handling large quantities of timber.

According to the figures, which were kindly obtained for me from Moscow in October, 1945, by their London Representative, the general forest area of the U.S.S.R. covers 933 million hectares, while the productive forest area covers 652 million hectares. The forest area of the Soviet Union may be divided into two main groups. In the first the dominant species are coniferous and consist of 390 million hectares. In the second are the deciduous forests which cover 130 million hectares while 132 million hectares remain unclassified.

It is interesting to note that out of 180 million hectares of developed forest, 74 million hectares are set aside, unfelled, for purposes of water preservation.

Stocks of standing timber are reckoned at 41 milliard cubic metres, and of these 35 milliard cubic metres are coniferous and 6 milliard cubic metres deciduous.

Of the estimated annual wood increment of 650 million cubic metres, only about 300 million cubic metres is cut—in

1940 273·2 million cubic metres were exploited—and of this figure about 150 million cubic metres is marketable timber, excluding firewood.

The greater part of the forest wealth of the Soviet Union is to be found in the distant regions of Siberia and the Far East, the exploitation of which is attended by considerable difficulties. However, in the last few years the main areas for timber production have been changed from the west and central parts of the U.S.S.R. to the north and to Siberia.

The coniferous forests alone comprise about one-third of the world's forest lands, for they extend 3,600 miles from west to east and 600 miles from north to south. The forests in Asiatic Russia are mainly situated in Siberia. They are very variable in character and contain much *taiga*, or swamp forest, while vast areas have suffered from the ravages of fire.

The following is an extract from *Soviet and Tsarist Siberia*, by Dr. George Borodin, published by Rich and Cowan: "Timber for the World! There is enough and to spare in Siberia. And the great point about it is that the Soviet Government is allowing nothing to interfere with its conservation. The policy of the Timber Trust is to ensure that the disasters which have occurred elsewhere in the exploitation of forest land are not repeated. Each year timber authorities, advised by surveyors, schedule so many trees for felling—and not only so many trees, but the actual trees to be cut. This figure is not exceeded. Any forester who cuts down an unscheduled tree is subject to severe penalty. And for every tree cut down, a new one is planted. Thus, by wise planning at every stage, the richest natural wealth of northern Siberia is being preserved. There will be no denudation or deforestation, with its economic consequences and its devastating effect on climate. But the policy in no way restricts the flow of wood into the mills. The rate of consumption might be doubled, or even trebled—as it may have been under the stress of war—but there would still be no risk of deforestation. The areas of England and France put together would not be sufficient to cover the Siberian forest lands, which are constantly patrolled and watched, largely from the air, to preserve them in their best condition."

The northern forest is composed principally of Scots pine

with some admixture of spruce, larch, and fir, and more frequently white birch. Southwards the broad-leaved species are more apparent, oak becoming the prevailing timber and forming forests with beech, maple, ash, and elm as admixtures. As the plains are approached, the forests become almost entirely broad-leaved. The northern slopes of the Crimean mountains are clothed with oak and the small-leaved hornbeam on the lower slopes, and beech forests on the higher mountains. But the dry limestone tops of the ranges are treeless. The southern slopes have many evergreen trees, including the juniper, cypress, and cedar of Lebanon. The middle slopes are clothed with oak, and the highest parts with pine. In the Caucasus the forests are chiefly coniferous, although on the lower slopes oak, ash, pear, apple, and maple may be found, with alder and willow in low-lying and damper situations. Beech forests cover large areas of the upper slopes, and oak, hornbeam, ash, lime, and maple are common. The beech forests are generally pure, providing thick canopy and a forest floor covered with mosses, while in the clearings are found azaleas and thick ferns. The high mountainsides are covered with the dark green of pine forests or giant firs, some of which reach a height of 180 feet.

The first recorded attempt to bring the Russian forests under management is attributed to Michael, founder of the House of Romanoff, and to Alexis II, who became Tsar in 1645. They, as a first step, provided protection against theft and fire. The successor of Alexis II, the far-seeing Peter the Great, inaugurated a long-reaching programme aimed at the more economic use of wood and the formation of forest reserves. Perhaps it was while he was working as a shipwright in Amsterdam that he found his first love for wood and a desire to build a navy for his own country. During his travels in Germany and other European countries, he probably studied forestry and the laws of conservation, and so returned to his own land equipped for the great task to which he set himself. At all events, on his return to Russia he began to reserve growing stands of ship timber, and all forests for a depth of thirty-five miles along rivers were placed under a newly organized administration of Crown forests. He built his famous Don flotilla on the River Voronezh, and used it to assist his southern expansion, for the forests provided the timber for the construction of his ships. Ample regulations were introduced to deal with the economic utilization of timber of all sorts. It is significant that the use of the saw instead of the axe was advocated and enforced.

Although there was a short setback to this good beginning when Peter's wife, Catherine I, influenced by her minister, Menshikoff, abolished the forest administration laws, the situation was saved when these laws were re-enacted under Anna Ivanovna and many new prescriptions for the proper use of wood were added. In 1727 a forest expert, Fökel, was appointed, and reafforestation was inaugurated by the sowing of acorns in the most poorly wooded districts. Planting was enforced, not only in the lands under the administration, but also upon privately owned lands, and, if the owners were neglectful, their lands were confiscated and reafforested by the forest administration. The laws restricting felling were abolished again by Catherine II in 1788 and, much to the concern of the Admiralty, the supply of ship timber was threatened. No further restrictive measures were imposed, however, but rather an ameliorative policy was attempted; for example, prizes for plantations were offered by some provincial governors. When Alexander II abolished serfdom of the peasants in 1861, he allotted land to them and in some parts as much as from twenty-five to fifty per cent of the forest land was handed over to them. Then followed a general slaughtering of the trees both by peasants and by the private owners who had suffered by losing the services of the serfs.

By 1864 the destruction had become so widespread that a movement for reform was begun by the Tsar who restricted acreage that might be felled, prohibited clearings, and gave premiums for good management and plantations. In 1875 a special commission was appointed to elaborate a general order, and, after years of hearing testimony and of deliberation, promulgated in 1888 a comprehensive law for the conservation of all forests.

The devastation and its effect on water flow and soil conditions had been most felt in the southern districts adjoining the steppe, and these experiences were the immediate cause for the enactment of the forest law which was then framed for the whole of European Russia. This law established that all forests protecting shifting sands and dunes, binding the shores of rivers, canals, and other waters, and those on the slopes of mountains, where they served to prevent landslides, erosion, and avalanches, should be managed by the Crown forest departments under special plans prepared by its forest officers. All forests classed as protective forests were strictly preserved. In other forests clearing for farms was permitted, but this was only allowed if the soil and lie of the land was fit for orchards and vineyards. If it was fit for farm use, permission was granted for temporary cultivation on the condition that it was eventually reafforested. This was only allowed, however, if another formerly farmed parcel of the same size had been reafforested at least three years before the proposed clearing. These regulations, although very exacting, were carried out in a thoroughly democratic spirit. Local committees were formed in each province and district, composed of various representatives of local administration, including foresters, justices of the peace or other justices, the county council, and two elected forest-owners. In all there were from nine to eleven members, under the presidency of the governor. It was such committees that decided which areas were to be included in protective forests. They approved of the working plans for these forests as well as for the unreserved lands. They determined which clearings might be made and exercised wide police powers, with reference to all forest matters. The forest administration drew up working plans for the reserve forests free of cost. The same body of forestry experts prepared working plans for the private owners, who, however, paid for them. Owners were permitted to prepare their own plans, but they had to be submitted to their provincial forest committee.

Forestry legislation was not entirely one-sided, for all protective forests were freed from taxes for ever. Those artificially planted were not taxed for thirty years, while any expenses arising from measures ordered might be charged to the government. Some of the more expert forest officials were detailed to give free advice to forest owners. Prizes were given for the

A Russian birch wood.

Timber being floated down the
river Pruth.

On the next two pages:
A close-up of lumbering in
Sweden.

"In Switzerland the forests are regarded as most important"—
Lauterbrunnen, where the trees prevent avalanches.

best results of silviculture operations. On the recommendation of the forest committees, medals, money rewards, and other distinctions were given to the forest guards and forest managers of private as well as public forests. Plants were distributed free or at cost price, and working plans for protective forests were made free of charge. Long-term loans could be arranged through the Imperial Loan Bank on condition that conservative management was assured. In a single year 7 million acres were in this way mortgaged under such management.

In Russia, forestry education goes back as far as 1782, when a number of foresters were imported from Germany to take charge of the forest management and train foresters. Each *Forstmeister* had six pupils assigned to him. This method apparently failed to produce results, and so, because of the great interest in ship timber, a course in forestry was started at the Naval Academy in 1800. The growing need of foresters led to the formation of separate forestry schools at Zarskoye Selo, at Kozlovsk, and at St. Petersburg. This last absorbed the other two and became the first Forest Institute. Soon it had as many as fifteen professors and instructors conducting a four-year course, preparing students for the higher positions in the forestry service. Other forestry schools followed, and ten secondary schools were established for rangers and under-foresters. By the beginning of the twentieth century the number of schools had increased to thirty. These were boarding schools in the woods, where a certain number of students were taught free of charge. The course of two years was mainly directed to practical work and theoretical study in silviculture.

Forestry experimental stations were set up in various parts of the country by the Administration of Crown Lands, and a very considerable and advanced literature is evidence of the good education and activity of the forest service. Two main forestry journals and several lesser ones kept the profession informed. There were several societies for the encouragement of silviculture. Probably the oldest was the Imperial Russian Society for the Advancement of Forestry. This was founded in 1832, and remained active until 1850. It published a journal and translated foreign books, among which was *Forest Mathematics*, by the noted German forester, König, who later prepared yield tables for the Society, based, not on the growth of a single tree, but on entire stands per acre classified by species. These yield tables were the first of their kind ever produced, and foresters the world over are to-day indebted to the far-sightedness of this old Russian Society for the pioneer work done by König. The first society for professional foresters was founded in St. Petersburg as far back as 1871. There was another in Moscow and others were founded later.

Theodor Karlowitsch Arnold was outstanding among the early Russian writers and practitioners, and is recognized as the father of Russian forestry. He was the soul of the forest organization work, and, first as professor and afterwards as Director of the Institute for Agronomy and Forestry at Moscow, he finally became head of the forest department in the Ministry of Appanages, where he remained until his death in 1902. Arnold was the author of several classical works on silviculture, forest mensuration, and forest management. In conjunction with Dr. W. A. Tichonoff, he published an encyclopaedic work in three volumes. In the first volume, *Russia's Forest*, the author made an extended plea for improved forestry practice. In 1895 he published a history of forestry in Germany, France, and Russia.

Among other prominent foresters who have advanced forestry in Russia should be mentioned Count Vargaci de Bedemar, who made the first attempt to prepare Russian growth and yield tables in the middle of the nineteenth century. Professor A. F. Rudzsky devoted volumes to the mathematical branches and methods of forest organization. The names of Tursky, Kravchinsky, and Kaigodorov are known to Russian students of dendrology and silviculture, and, among a later generation, those of Morozov, Nestorov, Orlov, and Tolsky may be mentioned. Russian investigators have become prominent in the natural sciences, and the work of the soil physicists, Otozky and Dokuchaev, are familiar to foresters.

The Russians were among the first to study the fundamentals of erosion control. Great was the success that attended the early planting of trees for shelter-belts by immigrants who settled in the Steppe Region in the early nineteenth century. Later plantings between 1880 and 1886 were on such a spectacular scale, with such excellent results, that a special Government commission was appointed to study afforestation on the Steppes. The objects placed before the commission included the protection of farms from wind, aid in the ripening of grain, more uniform distribution and retention of snow, raising the water table, modification of temperature, the attraction of rain, raising the productivity of waste unused lands, and control of soil erosion and drifting sands.

The Bureau of Deserts of the U.S.S.R. Institute of Plant Industry is making a special study of the reclamation of all the Russian deserts, of which the largest area is in Central Asia. The reclamation of shifting sands and sand-dunes has received considerable attention; also, to some extent, the reboisement of mountain slopes in the Crimea and the Caucasus. Of the former, some 10 million acres were completed, and 1,500 square miles of swamps in Western Russia were reclaimed by the formation of extensive canals, and reclothed with meadow and forest.

As in the U.S.A. and Canada, so in the U.S.S.R., the black earth lands are subject to soil erosion caused by the action of the wind or by heavy downpours of rain during the dry summers. It has been estimated that during the last twenty-five years 135 million acres of fertile black earth have been so removed and replaced by river sand. The Soviet Government has established a research station at Novosil, in the province of Tula, to deal with this problem. The obvious remedy has been found to be tree-planting, and where this has been done on a large scale it has been found that the yield of grain and grasses has increased considerably. Tree-planting has also been found to prevent the extension of gullies and ravines, and during the last twelve years nearly a million acres of new woods have been planted by the farmers in the U.S.S.R. The Russians were among the first to plant shelter-belts as wind-breaks in the Steppes, and their valuable pioneer work in finding the most suitable species has made a considerable contribution to that particular kind of reclamation work so necessary in Australia, Canada, and the U.S.A. The Russians have had a great deal of experience in planting shifting sands and sand deserts which were cultivated within historic times. Much is being done to-day to control the deserts by planting suitable vegetation on the sands, gradually establishing a green cover which will stop their movement. The saksaul tree, used for fuel, has been extensively planted, and apricot, wormwood, and the rubber-bearing plant, kok-sagyz, are being successfully grown.

The Russians have gigantic plans for land reclamation and rehabilitation, but World War II made vast inroads into their forests, and now, with the millions of homeless in that great country, still further timber must be sacrificed to build houses. An ever increasing planting programme will be required, not only to provide lumber for the rapidly-growing population, but as a safeguard against erosion. The vast majority of the inhabitants of the U.S.S.R. in the past have always been closely associated with farm and forest, and their inherent patriotism will doubtless enable them to continue in their conservative ways and set an example which all the world may follow.

Chapter Ten

SILVICULTURE IN CENTRAL EUROPE

*Silviculture is the art and science of perpetuating the woods
and forests for the service of man for all time.*

EVERY COUNTRY IN EUROPE HAS MADE ITS OWN PARTICULAR
contribution to silviculture. The study of the development of the science of forestry in Europe shows man's
progressive use of land throughout the centuries. Consciously
or unconsciously, the most economic methods have been
adopted, and here the art of silviculture has reached the
highest and most intensive application. There are countries
in Europe in which we can follow all the phases of development through which newer countries have passed or else will
eventually have to pass in the story of their evolution. We can
witness successive generations of Europeans who have, by
trial and error, by research and experiment, and by hard
necessity managed the adjustment of dense human occupation
of the land without destruction of the land's productive
capacity. Down throughout the ages the forest has been an
essential feature in the problem of land utilization and has
profoundly influenced not only a country's own well-being,
but that of the peoples of other countries of the world who have
followed the example of European practice.

Germany is known among foresters as the fatherland of
forestry. This country has long been regarded by informed
observers as the most advanced in the science of silviculture.
For many years it was my privilege to study forestry throughout Central Europe, originally in company with my fellow
students and later when conducting parties of foresters and
research students under the direction of Continental professors
of forestry.

To the French belongs the credit for having first recognized
the indirect benefits of the forest, such as its influence on
climate, its water-conserving effects, and its aesthetical and
general cultural influences and values. It was Leonardo da

Vinci who first interested Louis XII in forestry, which resulted
in the birth of European silvicultural systems. Leonardo's interest in growing trees may have been prompted by his research into the properties of wood, for it was he who invented
the first key for the identification of timbers. When I was preparing a key for the identification of European woods, I found
I could not do better than take Leonardo da Vinci's as a basis
for my work.

The conservation movement, which started in France, was
well established by the end of the eighteenth century, but it
was not until the end of the first quarter of the nineteenth
century that this movement made any impression on Germany.
However, the roots of German forestry reach back beyond the
Middle Ages, and traces of it may be found as far back as 1,000
years before Christ. It was then that Aryan tribes from Central
Asia began to overrun the country. These belonged to the
Celtic or Gaelic race, which had gradually come to occupy
part of the whole of France, Spain, Northern Italy, the western
part of Germany, and the British Isles. These were followed
by the Germani, meaning "neighbour" or "brother", also
Aryan tribes, who appeared at the Black Sea about 1000 B.C.
and in Switzerland and Belgium about 100 B.C. These were
followed by the Slovenes and the Slovaks, or Wends, who took
land left by the Germani. These early settlers found the mountainsides clothed with evergreen or broad-leaved trees, but their
first thought was to make clearings for farms and fields for
herding their cattle. Soon they began to suffer from drought,
and some of the tribes were faced with famine. Tradition relates
how they called upon their gods for rain, but their prayers
were of little avail. After a time some of the tribesmen
made the discovery that on the other side of the hills, where
the slopes were still green with trees, the rain fell in abundance. Their provident instinct prompted them wisely to
leave covering on the hills so that the fertility of the valleys
might be retained. Their inherent reverence for trees was
revived.

Sir James Frazer has shown that tree worship was well established in all the great European families of Aryan stock. Amongst
the Celts, the oak-worship of the Druids is familiar to everyone,

and their old word for sanctuary seems to be identical in origin
and meaning with the Latin *nemus*, a grove or woodland glade.
Sacred groves were common among the ancient Germans, and
severe were the penalties exacted for damaging the bark of
growing trees or felling protective groves. The native regard
for woods and forests prevented the inhabitants of these
countries from committing wholesale destruction, and their
love of the chase caused them to create forest reserves. Indeed,
by the end of the eighth century the word *Forst*, which until then
had been used merely to denote the King's property, was exclusively used to designate any territory in which the hunt had
been reserved. Not all the areas called *Forst* were woodland,
for real woodlands were known as *silva*, or *nemus*.

The beginnings of German silviculture have been traced
back long before the Middle Ages, when the so-called *Hack-
waldbetrieb* system of alternate field crops and oak coppice was
introduced in the Oldenwald, in the valley of Sieg, in the Saar,
and along the Moselle River. In some of the thickly settled parts
of western Germany and Austria the forests came under
production as early as the twelfth and thirteenth centuries.

The discovery that conifers could be easily introduced over
large areas led to the early introduction of a clear-cutting
system which preserved single trees or groups of seed trees, the
minimum number of which was prescribed. Under the influence of Hartig (1764–1837), organizer of the Prussian
State Forest Service, the Germans developed the orthodox
high-forest management of beech, the so-called shelter-
wood system. The same system was adopted a little later in
the spruce forests owing to the severe damage from windfall.
Thus it gradually came about that a large part of the German
forests were clear cut and planted in the latter half of the nineteenth century. The methods of artificial regeneration varied.
Plantations of conifers were made from the seventeenth
century. Ball-planting of pine was recommended in Prussia
in the latter half of the eighteenth century. Other methods of
artificial regeneration included mound-planting, *Hügelpflan-
zung*, and wedge-planting, *Klemmpflanzung*. Up to the end of
the eighteenth century the number of species was limited to
the indigenous varieties such as oak, beech, pine, larch, and

spruce, but these foresters were looking for rapidly growing species to restock the devastated and open portions of their forests. The German troops who fought in the American War of Independence brought home the knowledge of many fast-growing exotics, and, stimulated by a few enthusiasts, large numbers of foreign trees were experimented with; but it was found that the climatic and soil requirements were not sufficiently well known to make them succeed. Only *Pinus strobus*, *Quercus rubra*, and *Fraxinus americana* have survived out of the many plantations made at the time.

It was not until the first half of the nineteenth century that the sustained-yield principle dominated the German system of forest management. It was progress, indeed, to have reached this high ideal; but when, after the Industrial Revolution, wood had changed from a carefully rationed, essential material to an ordinary commodity, the production of which came to be governed largely by financial considerations, the forests were prostituted for profit. Conifers produced the best financial returns, and in consequence they were grown more and more to the exclusion of broad-leaved trees. Certainly there was at first an increase in the financial returns, but the even-aged plantations of a single species were contrary to Nature. Before long serious defects were obvious: there was soil deterioration and decreased rate of growth. This system of monoculture lessened the trees' resistance to animal and plant parasites and increased the risk to injuries from snow-break and wind.

Not until foresters began to gain a better knowledge of the natural sciences was the policy reversed. It was Professor Karl Gayer, silviculturist at the University of Munich, who in the last quarter of the nineteenth century led a new school of thought which revived some of the practical common sense that had been forgotten in the rush for financial returns. Gayer demanded that the forest be treated in accordance with biological laws instead of the schematic culture of pure stands. He advocated the reintroduction of broad-leaved species, especially beech, and natural regeneration, instead of clear cutting with artificial seeding or planting; the uneven-aged form of forest in place of even-aged stands was part of his teaching. His influence instigated one of the most promising developments of

"Green Gold of the North"—a Norwegian spruce forest in winter.

Sweden, too, understands the importance of wind-screening by trees.

forestry in Germany. Of course, there were mixed hardwood forests that survived the craze for conifers; for instance, in the Spessardt district of Germany I have walked for two and a half days through fine forests of oak and beech which had been run on a 320-year rotation for centuries.

Some European countries have been slow in learning from Germany's mistakes, and they are liable to follow slavishly outworn German systems now discarded in the country of their origin. A tragic example of this may be seen in Britain, where the countryside is being ruined by monocultures. Large areas have been afforested with even-aged plantations of a single species, chosen because it was fast-growing or especially suitable for pit props, without paying heed to the natural factors that control the life of the forest. Britain is not the only country to have fallen into this error, which proved to be costly enough to Germany half a century ago, and this should be a lesson for the rest of the world, too.

Austrian forestry has been influenced by German thought to a large degree, but it has not followed the mathematical systems of the Fatherland too strictly. When I was visiting the forests of Austria I was impressed by the flexibility of their silvicultural systems. They were adverse to stem mixtures, but planted in groups following the contour of the land. They planted the moist pockets with moisture-loving species and the steep hillsides with alpine varieties. Their working plans were frequently revised in the light of what they learnt from practical experience. These Austrian foresters were artists rather than economists, and they carried on much research in the most advanced forest practice. An important branch of Austrian forestry was carried out by the forest protective service, which consisted of the reboisement of mountains for the regulation of torrential streams. One of the best examples of the spirit of the Austrian policy and of the methods of forest organization and administration is to be found in the provinces of Bosnia and Herzegovina. A survey showed the forest area to be $6\frac{1}{4}$ million acres, fifty-one per cent of the land area. The most notable work of the Austrian foresters for the past seventy-five years was that of reafforesting the Karst or waste lands in the mountain and hill country of Istria, Trieste, Dalmatia, Montenegro, and adjacent

G

territory skirting the Adriatic Sea. It is a dry limestone country of close on a million acres, stony and rough. Originally it was well forested with hardwoods and conifers, and for ages it furnished ship timber and other wood supplies to the Venetians. Through reckless cutting, burning, and pasturing by the small farmers, it had become almost entirely denuded. For centuries countless laws were passed to stop the progress of devastation, without effect; but thanks to the initiative of the Austrian Government and the Forestry Association of that country, these areas are now under forest management.

In Czechoslovakia I was impressed by the enthusiasm of many large landowners who not only made forestry their hobby, but their life's work. They had built up rural industries and had formed prosperous communities working the products of the forest. Forestry requires particular skill in the mountainous region of the north-western part of that country. To reduce the speed of the wind and the consequent risk of windfalls, rides are cut up the mountainsides dividing compartments of growing trees. The foresters explained to me that the size of each compartment was controlled by a series of factors which checked the speed of hurricanes. By providing correctly placed vents in the form of open rides, the speed of the wind could be reduced to a point of safety. Although much of this is coniferous country, I saw the finest beech forest in Europe in Czechoslovakia.

Every country has a different approach to the science of silviculture. In Switzerland the forests are regarded as most important for the part that they play in preventing avalanches and for holding the soil on the mountainsides. The total forest area of Switzerland is 1,029,000 hectares, which corresponds approximately to twenty-five per cent of the total area of the country. There are no virgin forests, because all forests are worked on an intensive yield basis. The only exception to this rule is made by a number of forestry reserves which are placed under the supervision of a special Government Department and in which any cutting down of trees is forbidden. An example is the Swiss National Park in the Engadine, with an area of 16,000 hectares. The majority of the cultivated areas were gradually gained from the erstwhile wooded territory. The relations between agriculture and forestry are generally good. The farmers are very often themselves owners of forests or interested directly in the administration of publicly-owned forests. Experience has taught them that excessive exploitation of forests is always prejudicial to crops which are efficiently protected by forests against rapid changes of temperature, against violent winds, desiccation, and frosts.

Belgium is a splendid example of an industrial country which has retained interest in its forests. The total forest area at the last census, which was taken in 1929, showed a forest area of 541,140 hectares, or approximately 2,089 square miles. This area represents almost eighteen per cent of the land surface of the country. It is significant that 341,347 hectares carry broad-leaved trees and only 199,793 hectares coniferous. The species used for artificial reafforestation are spruce, Scots and Corsican pine, and Japanese larch. There are beautiful natural forests of beech in Belgium, one of the finest of which is located a little way out of Brussels, Forêt de Soignies, near Trevune. Near here, too, is one of the most outstanding forestry arboretums in Europe. It was created largely by prisoners of war during the First World War through the skill of a well-known Belgian forester who persuaded the Germans to allow him to carry out this work. Instead of planting individual trees, as is usual in an ordinary arboretum, groups of trees of a single species were planted over a large area, and each year these groups were enlarged until the whole converged to make a forest.

Of the total land area of the Netherlands, namely, 3,298,629 hectares, only 258,482 hectares, or nearly eight per cent, is forest. In the beginning of the nineteenth century practically all woods consisted of foliage trees. Since then the Scots pine has won ground, as this species is particularly suitable for afforestation of poor waste land. The Dutch found that the establishment of pine forests was neither difficult nor expensive, and the large demand for mine props in the second half of the nineteenth century also stimulated the extension of these forests. It was some time before the people became aware of the importance of afforestation; but in the second half of the nineteenth century, fear arose that the larger proportion of all forests in the country would soon disappear, and the conviction established itself that a permanent forest policy, directed or supervised by the Government, represented a national interest. In 1888 some far-seeing private persons established the Netherlands Heath Society, following the example of Denmark. The Society did much for the reclamation of waste land, and also promoted afforestation. In 1897 the Government revised the policy of selling common and Crown lands, an Act was passed for the purchase of 2,000 hectares of blowing sands and heath at Kootwijk, and the Heath Society was charged with the afforestation of this area. It was not until 1899 that the Government Forestry Service was inaugurated for the purpose of administering the Government-owned forests and to afforest waste land. In 1907 the Service was empowered to undertake afforestation on behalf of municipalities, and, if necessary, give financial assistance. In 1922 a new Forestry Act was enforced to widen the powers of the Government in this province, and in 1928 a law was passed for the protection of beauty spots. Since the Service was established, over 20,000 hectares of new forests have been planted, mostly on waste soil of which only a small proportion was already wooded.

The people of the Duchy of Luxembourg are proud of their trees, and it was under the French Revolutionary Government that the *Département des Forêts* was formed. Their oak trees have been the foundation of one of Luxembourg's oldest industries, that of tanning, and trees have provided the charcoal for smelting their iron. During the German invasion their forests were despoiled and the national riches in timber were greatly impaired. Reafforestation will, therefore, take an important place in their programme of reconstruction.

Denmark is largely a farming country, and only about nine per cent is regarded as forest. The surface of the country is uniformly low and flat, and presents little variety; all the same, it does not give an impression of monotony, because the landscape is enriched by noble forests, green meadows, and fertile fields. Not long ago the centre and west of Jutland were nearly bare of woods, but in recent years there has been a progressive planting programme. The beech forests are a great feature in the landscape which they dominate. In the old days oak comprised their main woodlands, but these are now comparatively

Sabine—from the painting by Vagaggini.

The Judean Hills, which will soon be once again clothed with Jerusalem pines and cypress.

rare. Pine has been mainly planted on the dunes and sand wastes. Artificial reproduction is the most general silvicultural practice, except in the beech forests, which are reproduced naturally after the preparation of the soil. Acorns are sown to provide a mixture. The Forestry Association of Denmark consists largely of forest-owners, and their forest literature and works on land reclamation are among the most valuable published in Europe.

The British Isles in the days of the reign of King Canute of Denmark was still a forest country, for they had not suffered from the invasion of the Romans. But to-day less than five per cent of the total area of Great Britain can be classed as forests. Both world wars have ravaged the woodlands, 800,000 acres falling to the axe in the First World War, and, before any sort of recovery could be made, a million acres had to be sacrificed to meet the needs of World War II. Following recommendations made by the Forestry Commission, it is proposed to plant five million acres during the next fifty years.

It would not be fitting to conclude this chapter without reference to one of the most striking examples of land reclamation which has taken place in Europe during the past century. The planting of the so-called Landes eastward of the great sand-dune region of Gascony in south-western France has now become a classic example to students of forestry in all parts of the world. This area consisted of a territory, triangular in shape, containing two million acres of shifting sands and marshes, on which a few poor shepherds used to eke out a precarious living, getting about as best they could on stilts. In 1837 an engineer of the administration of bridges and roads had the inspiration of improving this section by reafforestation, and at his own expense recovered some 1,200 acres in the worst marsh by ditching and planting. His great success encouraged others to follow his example, and in due course the results of the planting became so spectacular that the attention of the Government was aroused. A law was passed to enforce planting, and in time 1,750,000 acres were covered with fine forests. They planted the maritime pine and Scots pine. As a result of this land reclamation by reafforestation, the whole countryside has been transformed, and, in place of the poor shepherds, flourishing communities are now to be found.

Perhaps the greatest contribution that French foresters have made to the science of silviculture has been in the sphere of thinning operations. The French were among the first to understand the science of thinning, and it was they who put forward advanced theories which in later years became generally accepted.

The major task of the art and science of silviculture is to provide man with indispensable products, to maintain tree cover on those soils which by reason of their physical characteristics can only be used for forests, and at the same time assure the advantages of a well-balanced natural economy in respect of climate and hydrography, without which a lasting civilization is impossible. It is gradually coming to be universally recognized that the art and science of forestry can make the greatest possible contribution to the existence of man on this planet, for it serves life and provides the essentials to support life. This science deals with the problems of forestry and forest policy, beginning with the need for the more economic harvesting of what the forest yields, and extending to vital questions of the importance of forestry and its adjustment to the material and spiritual welfare of mankind. It is concerned with the needs of everyday life in every country, and it is called to serve every country by pointing the way for practising foresters. The experiences of the older countries with sustained-yield forestry may encourage or warn. They may show the road to scientific management and prevent the waste of time and money through falling into proven errors. Nowhere else on earth is there such a fund of experience in silviculture over so long a period of time as in Central Europe.

The principles of silviculture are capable of universal application, but it is essential to have a knowledge, in the first place, of forest ecology, or the science of forest sites, which rests on soil science and meteorology together with their basic and accessory disciplines. It is therefore the duty of each country and state to adapt the general principles to their own particular needs.

Chapter Eleven

GREEN GOLD OF THE NORTH

We had better be without gold than without trees.

John Evelyn.

SWEDEN IS ONE OF THE MOST WOODED COUNTRIES IN THE world. The forests cover half the total area of the country and are a primary source of wealth, giving work to hundreds of thousands of those sturdy people who make their livelihood from the trees. This country is of greatest interest to the world at large in forestry matters, because her export of forest products, lumber, wood-pulp, and paper is, next to Canada's, the largest in the world, and yet, in spite of that fact, it was only in this century that Sweden became aware of her need for a conservative forest policy.

This country, with 172,876 square miles, occupies the eastern two-thirds of the Scandinavian Peninsula. It is not mountainous like Norway, but the greater part consists of low granite hills. It is cut into numerous watersheds, the many rivers furnishing means of transport and providing water power. Little coal is to be found in Sweden, but she is called the kingdom of "white coal"—the "white coal", which has electrified her railroads and brought light and power to her farmers, comes as a by-product from the forests. This "white coal" is the power of water. These same waters which bring wealth to the soil pulsate with power, which is harnessed for the use of man. One purpose supplements the other in fulfilling the destiny of the waters as they flow on their way to the sea. The forest is the mother of the rivers, and the rivers are the roads of exit and yield the power for industry.

Here is an example of perfectly balanced economy which is brought about by the interplay of the principal natural resources. The forests have delivered the charcoal needed for the refining of ore into the steel for which Sweden is world-famous and the water-power has greatly aided the processing of the timber into lumber, pulp, and paper. Formerly many forests were utilized mainly in mining. Before the advent of gunpowder, men used to heat the rock and then cool it rapidly by pouring water over it, the contraction causing the ore-bearing rock to split. In this way enormous quantities of wood were required, and great volumes of timber were also converted into charcoal to be used in the blast furnaces for reducing the ore into pig-iron. During the seventeenth and eighteenth centuries this part of Sweden provided the world with a considerable portion of its iron and steel, and it was in those days that the foundation was laid for the international reputation of Swedish steel. Present-day mills in Bergslagen still use charcoal in steel-making, and "charcoaling" is an important source of employment. The cultivated soil extending into the forest area has moulded a hardy population accustomed to a life in the woods and highly skilled in logging.

The care of the forest has now become the concern of all the Swedish people, in order that the forest yields may be sustained and further improved. The visitor travelling through the southern part of Sweden will find a landscape where fertile farms are interspersed with wooded hills and mountain ranges, the ridges displaying the bare primary rock which serves as the foundation of the entire Scandinavian Peninsula. In this rock will be seen traces left by glaciers which thousands of years ago scooped up the loose earth of the mountain ridges and deposited it in the valleys below. Following the Ice Age, this was submerged by the post-glacial sea, which deposited the layers of clay now constituting the fertile farmland of the country. The Dal River forms the line of demarcation between the two principal forest regions in Sweden, the northern and southern coniferous regions, and at the same time it also forms the northern limit of the oak, *Quercus pedunculata*. In the central part of Sweden proper the forest region begins with pine and spruce, covering the granite hills and plateau, birch and other hardwoods, oak, beech, elm, lime, and poplar being found in the river valleys. The Scots pine, *Pinus silvestris*, and Norway spruce, *Picea excelsa*, are the only indigenous conifers. They are often accompanied by some hardwoods, of which the birches, *Betula berrucosa* and *Betula pubescens*, are the most common. The white stems of the birch trees show up in pleasant contrast to the sombre character of the coniferous woods.

Norrland, with the northernmost part called Lapland, is a vast, almost unbroken, forest country with a sparse population. Here, too, pine and spruce, with white birch intermixed, are the trees of the country. Towards the northern boundary the white birch increases, and aspen, *Populus tremula*, are frequently found, until finally the treeless tundra appears. A treeless alpine region occupies the north-western frontier territory, fringed at lower elevations by a belt of birch. This part of Sweden is cut by the Arctic Circle, which is often considered the northern limit for forest growth. But in Sweden the forests continue north of the Arctic Circle because of the proximity of the Gulf Stream. However, where the land rises to any considerable height the influence of the Gulf Stream is not sufficient to provide the necessary temperature for forest vegetation, and the mountains of Lapland are therefore bare of trees.

This great northern forest region remained undisturbed until ninety years ago. Those great stands of pine and spruce had never been touched by man, except in the lower reaches of the rivers; along the valleys were little saw-mills. The golden age of the Swedish saw-mill industry began when timber tariffs in England and France were lifted. At first these forests suffered grievously, because the plums were taken; the prime timber was removed while the suppressed, dead, and dying trees were left. During the past thirty or forty years, however, public opinion in Sweden has changed all this. Cuttings have been made with due regard to silvicultural principles. Now the overmature and damaged trees are the first to be taken, and trees capable of further growth are retained, while mother seed trees are left to ensure regeneration. Thus the forest capital is maintained to yield its annual wood increment for the wealth of Sweden.

Norway has practically no virgin forest, apart from a few small areas in mountain valleys that have not yet been touched by axe. Almost all her woodlands are worked economically, with due regard for future yields, and by a new Forest Conservation Act of 1932 all felling is under professional control.

The total forest area in Norway is 7,499,033 hectares, or

approximately 29,300 square miles. The main species, which grow in her mountainous plateaux and along the sides of her deep valleys and lakes, and border her numerous fjords and waterways, are Norway spruce, *Picea abies*, Scots pine, *Pinus silvestris*, birch, aspen, oak, and elm. Fifty-three per cent of the whole forest area is covered by Norway spruce, twenty-eight per cent by Scots pine, while the remaining nineteen per cent consists of hardwoods. Two-thirds of the Norwegian woodlands belong to the farmers; this is a fact which is of great importance to the economic conditions, and helps to solve the question of employment in the rural districts. The surplus labour readily finds work on the farms in the summer, but winter months are naturally the busiest times in the woods, when the farmlands are frozen.

In Norway there are 4,500 saw-mills, generally fed by floating rivers. There is, however, plenty of scope for afforestation, because seventy-five per cent of the country is waste land, while only three per cent of the land is in farms. The most valuable portion, from the forest point of view, is the south-eastern corner around Oslo in eight counties, in which the forest area is as high as fifty per cent, going up to 3,000 feet elevation. Again in the three counties around Trondhjem a large and important forest area is located at the head of the fjords. The entire western coasts and the higher elevations are devoid of valuable forest growth, and the northern third of the country, north of the Arctic Circle, is mostly heath and moors, with only seven per cent wooded with inferior birch.

When I was staying at Mandal in South Norway, one evening I was walking along the coast with the late Lord Salvesen, and he pointed out to me a school plantation which had been made by successive generations of scholars. That same evening I went to a dance in the town of Mandal, and mentioned what I had seen to one of my partners, and she explained that each class in the school undertook to plant a given area. She invited me to see the plantation that her class had made fifteen years before when she was a girl at school. On visiting the forest with my new-found friend, I was interested to see that it consisted of about fifty small compartments ranging from one-year-old to fifty-year-old trees. It was customary for children to take their parents to see the trees of their planting, and in many cases the parents themselves could in turn show their children the trees which they had planted in a previous generation.

On a later visit to this hospitable country, I was lecturing before the Royal Norwegian Geographical Society when I met representatives of the Norwegian Forestry Society. They told me that much of the new work of afforestation was being carried out by the Norwegian Army, and that, during manœuvres, the soldiers were largely responsible for fire prevention. It is significant that Norway has treated the question of afforestation with such urgency that it is regarded as a vital part of military preparedness. Here is an example that all the armies of the world might well follow.

Finland, the land of fens and lakes, covers an area of 150,000 square miles, of which half is forest; only Russia and Sweden surpass her in the extent of their forest areas. About two-fifths of Finland's woods are owned by the State and are regulated by law. The forests consist principally of spruce and a variety of Scots pine called Riga pine, which is well known for its straight growth and clean bole. Aspen, alder, and birch, especially the latter, are considered forest weeds, and fire is often used to destroy them. Lime, maple, elm, ash, and some oak are to be found, and larch, *Larix Sibirica*, was introduced nearly two centuries ago. The long severe winters and hot dry summers of Finland produce slow growth, the pine in the north requiring 200 to 250 years, or in the middle sections 140 to 160 years, to grow to maturity. This slow growth, forming close annual rings, makes for high quality, and so the timber of Finland is always in great demand.

The Poles are a natural forest people, and it is the greatest ambition of every man to have a piece of land large enough to grow trees on—trees rather than flowers. The best wooded areas of Poland are those in the south and east, and especially in the Carpathians. The total forest area in 1937 was 33,298 square miles, 8,463,000 hectares, or 22·2 per cent; but the woodland area is decreasing in size. During the five years of German occupation two and a half to three times as much forest area was cut yearly as in pre-war days. Three-quarters of the forests are coniferous, and the remaining quarter deciduous.

But for the Bialowieza National Park there is little virgin forest in Poland; this area, however, has been protected in its primeval grandeur. In times gone by this forest was the scene of many royal hunting parties famous throughout Europe. This, too, is the last home of the European bison. Even now, after the damage wrought by war, this ancient forest retains its interest and charm for the scientist, forester, artist, and lover of nature. Outstanding among the tree species of Europe is the true silver fir, *Abies alba*. Poland has made two separate reservations for the protection of the last remaining rugged veterans. There is another National Park inside the Czarnohora, where the mountainsides are covered with a dark mantle of forests, with dwarf pines at high altitudes. Above the spruce region, from 4,000 to 5,000 feet altitude, is the realm of dark green mountain pine and juniper. And here may be found dwarf willows, but the tree that towers above the rest is the "limba", or stone pine. They grow very slowly and their wood is greatly valued by cabinet-makers, for it is immune to worms. These trees are becoming rare, for only on the slopes of Zabie, near Morskie Oko, and in the Jarorova Valley, do forests of them remain.

On the borders of Poland and Czechoslovakia, in the northern foothills of the Tatra Mountains, with all their natural grandeur, is a region of beech and spruce forest with some larch, ash, rowan, and pine. Standing out on many a mountain crag here, too, may be seen silver firs of great age. In autumn they form a fitting background to the dark red tints of the beech, which contrast with the gold of the larches, forming a magnificent picture. Such gems of beauty may not bring golden gain from lumber, but their aesthetic value is untold, for they speak to the very heart of man.

"There is no country in the world that would show greater response
to planting"—the harbour at Haifa.

"Reclothing bare and desiccated hill tracks"—a shelter-wood regeneration area in U.P.

Chapter Twelve

AMONG THE EVERGREENS

And here were forests ancient as the hills,
Enfolding sunny spots of greenery.

Coleridge.

A HUNDRED MILES SOUTH OF CAPE FINISTERRE BEGINS THE realm of the evergreen trees and shrubs, which at one time extended from the Atlantic coast eastwards to the eastern shores of the Black Sea. The peninsulas of the Mediterranean, together with the coastal strip of North Africa, are the natural home of many members of the great family of the evergreens. The people of these territories are much alike in character and temperament, and they represent the older civilizations. The Mediterranean shores were once the most populous in the world; but the vast forests which were the very foundation of the well-being of multitudes have disappeared from the mountain ridges, leaving bare rocky spurs and ledges. The humus, accumulated beneath the trees by the decay of leaves and fallen trunks, was washed away. The soil of the alpine pastures which were once surrounded by woods was destroyed. Meadows, too, that were green and fertile became waste and unproductive, because the once tree-surrounded reservoirs that supplied the ancient canals were broken or the springs that fed them dried up. Rivers famous in history have shrunk to mere brooklets or have widened into broad expanses of sand and gravel, which are dry in summer, but which in winter are transformed into raging torrents. Sand bars block the entrances of many navigable streams and harbours which once were centres of trade and commerce. Down through the ages their countries have been scarred by war, and in consequence all the accessible forests have grievously suffered. Internal unrest and lack of political stability and long-term policies have hindered the attempts that have been made towards conservation.

Proximity to the sea has enabled these countries to import

wood from elsewhere, so that they have not felt the need to adopt far-sighted afforestation policies.

In Italy from the earliest times the *lignarii*, or wood merchants, imported their supplies from as far-distant countries as India by way of Alexandria. For ash they went to Asia Minor, for cedar to Cilicia. In Cicero's time there was a regular wood market in Rome, as in Jerusalem, where wood was sold by the pound.

In the past, colonization, exploitation, fire, farming, and goats did away with most of the virgin forests. The plight of these countries might have been even worse, but, fortunately for them, they have largely escaped industrial development, and so they have not all seriously felt their forest deficiency, apart from suffering from droughts and floods. Spain is one of the countries that has suffered severely through deforestation. What a wonderful country the whole of the Iberian Peninsula must have been in ancient times, when it was richly clothed with evergreen trees! In the days when Rome was at the height of her power, it was a common saying that in Spain a bird could travel from one end of the country to the other by hopping from tree to tree. According to Diodorus Siculus, the southern provinces were densely wooded until 200 B.C., when the Romans first took possession. But a great forest fire starting from the Pyrenees ran over the country, exposing deposits of silver ore which invited a large influx of miners and which became the cause of reckless forest destruction. Forests were open to all, and when they were exploited there was no compulsion or inducement to reafforest. Woodland parks such as the paradises of the Persian kings and the *nemora* of the Romans and Carthaginians were early examples of reserves from which exploiters were excluded. Certain groves were regarded as sacred among the ancients. These were frequent in Greece and Italy, as also in other pagan countries. But even these were violated, as, for example, in Palestine at the time of Joshua's successful campaign, when the Israelites were enjoined to eradicate these groves with axe and fire.

Spain, once a paradise, became almost a desert through neglect, ignorance, indolence, despotism of Church, and misrule by corrupt bureaucracies. The fertility of much of the land was lost through soil erosion caused by high winds, which gathered force when the evergreen covering of the great forests was removed. Land prepared for tilling became sterile. In the early centuries of the Christian era a prosperous population of 40 millions exploited the country. Then came the dark days of Gothic rule, until a second period of prosperity was enjoyed, at any rate, by the sphere influenced by the beneficent rule of the Saracens, who reclaimed deserts and whose irrigation works are the mainstay of agriculture to the present day. Despite centuries of warfare and bloodshed in the effort to establish Christian kingdoms, the country still remained wealthy, when in 1479 the several kingdoms were united under Ferdinand and Isabella. With the discovery of America, yet another era of prosperity was enjoyed by the people, who had then dwindled to 20 millions. But the Inquisition, which also led to the expulsion of the Jews and wholesale emigration to America, undermined the prosperity of the country, and its population had declined to 10 millions by the beginning of the nineteenth century.

Throughout all this time the tree cover suffered, and at present the forest is mainly confined to the higher mountains. The most valuable are to be found in the Pyrenees and the Cantabrian Mountains. It has been said that in the past Spain has been noted for its comprehensive legislation without execution, and that official reports were rarely trustworthy. It was not until about 1833 that there was an awakening to the necessity for conservation. It was then that a law was enacted and an ordinance issued at great length, defining the meaning of *montes* and instituting forest inspection.

Some years later a number of young men were sent to the forest school at Tharaud in Germany, and it was probably under the influence of these men on their return, backed by *La Sociedad Económica* of Madrid, that a commission to formulate a forest law was instituted. In 1846 a school was established at Villaviciosa de Odon, which was later transferred to Escuriel, near Madrid. This school, organized on the German lines by Bernardo della Torre Royas, who became its first director, was quite deservedly the pride of Spanish foresters. The creation of a forest department, *Cuerpo de Montes*, followed, and a general forest survey was made. The forests owned by the State, the communities, and public institutions were divided into three classes according to the species of tree at the time: this appeared to be the easiest way of determining their locations as regards altitude and their public value. These were the coniferous forest, the deciduous oak and chestnut forests, and the forests of ash, alder, and willow, the last-named naturally situated in the lower levels. The first two classes of forest were declared preserves and were strictly protected, while the third class were declared saleable. There was an intermediate class composed of cork oak and evergreen oak whose status was left in doubt. Later on, revision of this classification was made. Together with all the forest areas of the first class which were not at least 250 acres in extent, it was added to the saleable class. The first class, which was to be reserved, was found to be approximately 17 million acres, of which over a million was owned by the State, while the saleable property was found to be about half that area. There followed constant disputes regarding the classification, and repeated attempts were made by different political factions to reduce the forest area. These were opposed by the forest administration, which was forced again and again to re-classify. As the forests became exploited under the Minister of Finance to meet immediate financial needs, the country suffered increasingly from floods and droughts. It so happened that when the sale, in annual instalments, of over $4\frac{1}{2}$ million acres was ordered by the Ministry of Finance, the same year there were disastrous floods causing great loss of life and property, and 28,000 people were made homeless. This was in turn followed by successive droughts. So stirred was the public sentiment that there was a revision of policy which led to the enactment of a reboisement law which ordered the immediate reafforestation of all waste land in the public forests. Alas! funds were not forthcoming, and by 1895 only 21,000 acres had been reafforested under this law, and three-quarters of this merely by sowing tree seed.

By the beginning of the twentieth century a new and more promising era was brought about when the technical administration of the forests was divorced from political influence and brought under the newly created Minister of Agriculture.

Popular education was attempted through arbor days, various associations fostering the idea, and in 1904 *La Fiesta del Arbol* was made a national holiday, and prizes were distributed for plantations made on that day. In time this educational campaign bore fruit, and now for over fifty years both government and private enterprise have made every effort to recreate old woodlands.

The plan implemented to bring this about has taken two courses. Directly in charge of this work is the Afforestation Section of the Ministry of Agriculture, headed by experts from the Forestry Corps. Their job is to conserve existing tracts of woodland, to create preserves, and to plant new woods. It is a never-ending task, and one which is catered for in every Government Budget. Over twenty years ago, in an effort to further and intensify this work, General Primo de Rivera's Government set aside a large sum of money. Political changes made it impossible for this financial assistance to be repeated in succeeding years, but in 1942 the Government again made a large appropriation to this end.

Private enterprise, inspired by the good financial prospects offered by the timber industry at the end of World War I, has also carried out some important afforestation programmes, which have been mainly concentrated in the north of Spain, where the climate is particularly suitable for this kind of cultivation.

Public interest in the Government's efforts has been aroused, in the first place, by the teachers in rural schools, who have made every effort to kill the centuries-old country prejudice against trees and imbue their pupils with a "tree-consciousness". This has been helped by the introduction of a "Tree Day", on which the children throughout the country plant their own little tree, to be tended and looked after by them during their play time and holidays.

Propaganda and the vigilance of forest-keepers have also helped to consolidate the State's authority and avoid wholesale tree-felling. At the same time, official undertakings have, where possible, given every help to firms interested in afforestation, but, lacking financial means, the results have not always been up to the measure of their hopes.

H

Portugal is the country of pines and cork oak. This small kingdom, which occupies the west coast of the Iberian Peninsula, with 36,000 square miles and 6 million people, is fortunate in having a larger proportion of fertile land than her larger neighbour. The northern section is mainly mountainous and has extensive sand-dunes, large areas of which have been reclaimed by tree-planting. The central part is hilly and not so well-wooded, although it contains some of the best-managed forests. In Estremadura, planted pines cover an area of 25,000 acres. The southern area, of semi-tropical climate and flora, is rich in farmlands and has extensive cork-oak plantations.

The entire forest area of the country, including brushwood and scrub forest, is perhaps under a million acres. Eighty per cent is coniferous, consisting of *Pinus pinaster* and *Pinus pinea*. The remaining twenty per cent is cork oak and other oaks mixed with Spanish or sweet chestnut, *Castanea sativa*. Cork from the bark of the cork oak is the principal export, and the pines are tapped for turpentine and resin, which are exported as naval stores.

Portugal's first attempt at the scientific management of her forests was made in the middle of the nineteenth century. However, a regular organization was not established until later, under a Director-General of Commerce and Industries. At the beginning of the twentieth century a more thorough organization of reafforestation was made, and allowed Government expropriations of waste lands in the interest of the public. The School of Agriculture in Lisbon is responsible for the education of the technical forestry staff.

The pine forests, whether natural or planted, possess a charm of their own. They have been described with great feeling by Evelyn Harbord, Schools' Secretary of the Men of the Trees, who knew them so well in pre-war days. She tells how they grow on the undulating plateau between two ranges of great mountains and, sloping southward, end at the feet of the highest mountain of the country, Serra da Estrela, the Mountain of the Star. It is this undulation that gives the forests their charm, the waving, mingling lines of many horizons, fading, dipping, rising like waves of a rough sea. In early morning the mists cling to the tree tops, pale and paler in the distance, and at sunset they look pink and soft as clouds. In such woods there are few birds, though in the clearings the nightingales sing loudly both by day and by night, and sometimes a pair of golden oriel will flash among the green. But the thickest parts of the forest are silent and still. Nothing disturbs the quiet except, perhaps, an old woodman trimming the trees or changing the earthenware pots on their trunks, which are put there to catch the turpentine. He loves his trees, and seems to belong to the forest and share its rhythm.

Forest destruction in every country spells disaster in one form or another. Whereas, for instance, in Africa it brings erosion and deserts and in Switzerland avalanches, in Italy the rivers are turned into torrents and floods by deforestation. In Italy, therefore, it was the urgent need of protecting their watersheds that induced efforts to secure economic forest management. But the enforcement of wise forestry laws involved national sacrifice, and so in the past it was found difficult to introduce any reform, and many a time when attempts were made to enforce protective measures serious trouble arose.

With her dense population of over 40 millions on 119,000 square miles, with over one-third of the country unproductive or unused and a large proportion of this incapable of being reclaimed, no country offers better opportunities for studying the disastrous effect of deforestation on soil and waterflow. The geology, topography, and climate are such that, once the forest cover is removed, disaster is certain. Slates and limestones on steep hills and mountainsides, when bared of trees and pastured by millions of goats, produce ideal conditions for bringing about the flooding of rivers. The melting snow and the heavy spring rains turn them into raging torrents.

About a quarter of Italy's forests are found in the Alps, and a further half are situated on either side of the Apennines, the backbone of this peninsula. Less than a third of her trees and woodlands are distributed over the mainland, while the balance are found on the islands. Sicily was once magnificently wooded, though it is now largely denuded, and Sardinia is still one of the best-wooded parts of Italy. High up in the Alps are the birch, spruce, fir, larch, and pine, and here and there in remote, unexploited spots in the tops of the Apennines a similar cover may still be found, although for the greater part these slopes are occupied by inferior brush forest, coppice, or open forest with scattered trees among rough scrub and thorns. Although there are few forests of any value in Italy, the country is by no means treeless, for poplar, ash, and elm are dotted over the plains and slopes, where they are often planted for vine supports and to mark boundaries. These trees are frequently mutilated by pollarding in a country where fire-wood is a scarce commodity. Olive plantations and chestnut groves cover 2 million acres of the lower slopes. Eight million acres in vine-yards, with their living vine supports, add to the wooded appearance of the country and provide fire-wood and charcoal for domestic and industrial purposes. Along the sand-dunes and near the seashore may be found the maritime and Aleppo pine and the umbrella-shaped *Pinus pinea*. Here, too, are the picturesquely erect Roman cypresses, which are seen in groups or small groves, while above, in a region up to 1,200 feet above sea level, are olives, cork oak, and evergreen oak. Osiers are grown for basket-making, while on the mountain-sides may be found forests of Scots pine, *Pinus silvestris* and *Pinus laricio*, with a large proportion of fir, *Abies pectinata*. Much of the hardwood forest is managed as coppice for the manufacture of charcoal.

In Southern Italy the vegetation takes on a tropical appearance, with its date palms, orange, lemon, and citron trees. The evergreen effect is intensified by the foliage of the laurels, myrtles, and oleanders, with forests of arbutus, or strawberry trees, and the evergreen oak.

For centuries, from the fall of the Roman Empire until the end of the eighteenth century, Italy has been the victim of war and strife with neighbouring countries, and, within her borders, has struggled vainly with the inevitable legacy of denuded lands. However, during the nineteenth century many efforts were made to introduce conservation laws. The devastating floods of 1882 led to much agitation for reboisement; but although laws were passed, they rarely received effective application. Yet the forest department persistently tried to promote reafforestation by giving prizes and distributing millions of young trees and quantities of seed from its nurseries and by furnishing free advice to planters.

It is interesting to note that Italy was the first country to celebrate the armistice after World War I by tree-planting. On that day the inhabitants of many a mountain village gathered to pay tribute to those whom they had loved and lost by planting trees in their names.

To two Italians is due the credit of having found that the true reason for the salubrity of forest air is the absence of pathogenic bacteria. It is also to the renown of Italy that she was one of the first to recognize by legislation the forest influence on health conditions. The belief that deforestation of the marshy lowlands between Pisa and Naples produced malarial fever, led the Trappist monks of the cloister at the Tre Fontane to make plantations of eucalyptus. But one of the greatest things Italy ever achieved in the forestry world was to convene the first World Forestry Congress, which was held at the International Bureau of Agriculture in Rome in 1926 and was attended by representative foresters from almost every country in the world. This Congress had its inception at my camp in the Highlands of Kenya, when Dr. Caviccioni, the Italian representative for East Africa, lunched with me and witnessed a march-past of the first *Watu wa Miti*, Men of the Trees. He had been impressed by the way in which warring tribesmen had responded to an appeal and banded themselves together to protect their vanishing forests, and to plant trees in their old farms to safeguard the forests of the future and the fertility of their lands. As, clan by clan, they passed before him, my Italian visitor became more and more enthused and excited, and exclaimed, "Baker, this is the *facista* of Africa! You must meet my friend Mussolini." At that time the march on Rome had not taken place and, although I accepted the Doctor's introduction to the Duce, I did not meet him immediately. But on my return to Europe I contacted a number of young men in Genoa and was able to interest them in the importance of my subject. They lost no time in getting to work, and the outcome was that three years later the World Forestry Congress took place in Rome.

As one of the delegates to this Congress, I accompanied

Professor Troup of Oxford and had the opportunity of meeting the many delegates who had arrived from all parts of the world. The usual procedure was to listen to each other's papers being read in the morning, and to devote the afternoons to expeditions into the Italian forests. Never before had the Italian Forestry Service such a splendid opportunity of exchanging views and gaining the expert advice of admitted masters in the art and science of forestry. The visitors, for their part, were interested to see what had been done by way of planting, sometimes under the most adverse conditions. One of the expeditions took us to Vallombrosa, where the first *Institute Forestale* had been founded in 1869. There we saw mountainsides which had once been bared of their forest growth and all their humus, but which were now re-clothed with great firs. We were told how monks used to chip holes in the sides of precipitous rocks, then fetch earth in bags from the valleys below, and into each pocket of soft humus tuck a tiny seedling until the mountainside was once again fixed and enjoying the green mantle of the firs. The name of this mountain village, once again tree-surrounded, brings to mind Milton's ". . . Leaves . . . In Vallombrosa", which may have referred to the sturdy beech trees that fix the soil of the mountain top above the firs planted by the thoughtful brothers in bygone centuries.

At that Congress the forestry representatives from every country pooled their sources of information and came to the conclusion that the world was heading for a timber famine which would be experienced within forty years. My subsequent world tour led me to regard this as a very conservative estimate, and the devastating effects of World War II may precipitate this foretold famine sooner than anticipated.

Greece was another country which in times gone by was richly clothed with evergreens. Originally the whole of this peninsula, with a few small exceptions, was a continuous forest. Under the régime of the ancient Greeks the forests were protected by thousands of woodland deities and nymphs of the holy groves, until the fanaticism of the early Christians led to a war against these pagan strongholds, in which the holy groves were destroyed by axe and fire. Centuries of misrule, over-taxation, reckless cutting, and extensive herding of goats and sheep, together with fires, have reduced the forest area until to-day it covers but 1,917,980 hectares, or 15·1 per cent of the whole area of that country. Indeed, there is no virgin forest left. The many islands are entirely deforested, and so are the seashores—where in olden times dense shady poplars stood—leaving a scene of barren sand and dreary rock.

The forest in northern and middle Greece is confined to the two mountain ranges which run parallel north and south with Mount Olympus and Mount Pindus as the highest elevations. The large plains of Thessaly and Bœotia are treeless; so is the large Arcadian plateau of the Peloponnesos; so, too, are the other smaller but fertile plains and plateaux. The most valuable conifer forest is found in the higher ranges between 2,500 and 5,000 feet, below the snow-clad mountain tops, where especially two species of fir, *Abies Apollinis* and *Abies reginae Amaliae*, with other firs and several species of juniper and cypress, form extensive forests. Other common trees are chestnut, sycamore, several species of oak, poplar, and, on the coast, *Pinus halepensis*. The firs occupy about one-third of the forest area, evergreen oaks and other evergreen trees another third, while the remaining area is deciduous.

The climate is favourable to tree growth, and the soil would readily reclothe itself if left alone. The winters are short with hardly any ice or snow, except on the high mountains, and trees will grow for nine months in the year. The temperature ranges from 20° to 160° F., the rainfall averages 400 millimetres, and, although the summers are rainless and dry, the other seasons are humid, and rapid growth results from these conditions. But the continued pasturing of millions of goats and sheep prevents any natural regeneration. The practice of permitting people to collect dry wood for fuel leads to forest fires, and perhaps nowhere are forest fires more frequent, in spite of heavy penalties. The forest destruction has had baneful influence on the water condition and river flow, and in no other country is a tree sense more badly needed.

During the enemy occupation of World War II the forests of Greece suffered great ravages. The destruction was effected on the one hand by over-felling carried out directly by the enemy to the extent of denuding certain forest areas, and, on the other, by the disintegration of the Hellenic organization and management. The great ravages were near cities or inhabited areas on bordering road or railway arteries. Further forest areas were sacrificed to accommodate thousands of refugees from Asia Minor, Thrace, and Russia after the Asia Minor disaster.

The great tragedy of Greece is that little is being done to restore her forests. It is the exception rather than the rule to find planters of trees amongst the people, although some forestry operations are carried out by officials of the State.

To many of the Balkan States their forests are a symbol of liberty: in Yugoslavia, for instance, the forests are not only an important factor in the national economy, but also a cherished motif in her national poetry. How great is the love of her people for the forest is shown by the fact that one of the most important Yugoslav provinces was named Sumadija, derived from the word *suma*, forest. Dr. Ljubo Leontić, Yugoslav Ambassador to the Court of St. James, addressing delegates to the World Forestry Charter Luncheon held in London in 1946, said that it was there in Sumadija that the flag of the national movement for liberation was first unfurled 140 years ago and where the liberation movement of World War II began and spread all over the country. He said: "It is not astonishing, therefore, that my people have looked to the forests as a stronghold of their liberty." That was why invaders would always start by cutting down the forests before attacking the people, in the hope that by so doing they would destroy the resistant forces.

Rumania has for many years developed her forestry systems over her 48,000 square miles, half of which are hilly and mountainous, and the remainder the rich, alluvial valley of the Danube. This latter is now largely deforested. The hill and mountain country was, until the eighteenth century, well wooded, but then it was sorely depleted to meet the demands of Turkish markets. The wars of this century have naturally made further inroads, and it has been estimated that but ten per cent of the total area of the country remains forest.

Bulgaria, with its 38,000 square miles, is fortunate in possessing extensive forests which comprise one-third of the total land area. Although it touches the zone of the evergreens, much of its forests consist of oak, beech, and walnut. In the past,

"This is the realm of great conifers"—Deodar, Himalayan Cedar, at Chakrata.

On the next two pages: a Himalayan forest.

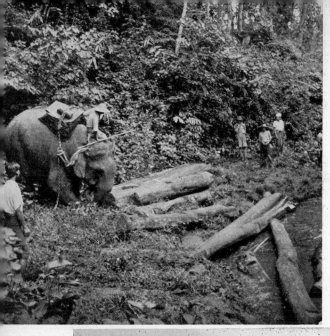

"It is fascinating
watch a big elepha
pick up a log"—in
Burmese teak forest

"Modern man
making increasi
demands on t
wealth of the
mighty forests."

waste, neglect, and mining requirements had stripped the country of many of the dense forests with which it was once covered. However, the more inaccessible woodlands still flourish in the north up to altitudes of over 2,000 feet; these are mainly of beech and oak, while many of the southern mountains are clad with conifers to well over 3,000 feet. Bulgaria is a fertile country, and with the introduction of more conservative measures might well maintain a much greater population.

Hungary has a total area of approximately 707,000 hectares containing the following species: oak, beech, hornbeam, acacia, ash, elm, poplar, willow, Scotch fir, black pine, and other firs. They have an active Forestry Department under the Minister of Agriculture, who takes care of regeneration. Forestry reserves are needed for her requirements, and some timber for building is imported from Rumania.

Following the realm of the evergreens, we come to Turkey, famous for her great number of species of forest trees. She has no fewer than eleven different kinds of oak, including evergreen oak and the well-known Turkey oak. Here, too, are the chestnut-leaved oak, which in the east provide food for the silk-worms producing shantung. There are five maples, four pines, four true firs, and six junipers, which strike an evergreen note wherever grown. These and many other forest trees cover a total area of 10,500,000 hectares, 300,000 hectares of which represents virgin forest.

Although in the past the forests of the Ottoman Empire have suffered under misrule, in more recent times an effort has been made to work the forests on a sustained yield basis. Two methods are now used for regeneration: natural regeneration and planting. Cleared spaces of the forest are regenerated through the process of natural regeneration, while the planting is used to develop green belts around villages which have no forests of their own. This latter planting started in 1934, and in that year 52 hectares were planted, in 1944, 1,157 hectares, and in 1945, 1,438 hectares; and so it may be seen that a steady planting programme is in progress. Natural regeneration was started in 1945, and in the following two years an area of 100 hectares was regenerated. Great credit is due to those who have inspired this recent forestry development.

Palestine has been described as a bridge between Asia and Africa, but this actually applies only to the maritime plain. This was the great route followed by many an invading army, as well as by trade and commerce throughout the centuries. From Egypt it enters Palestine at Gaza and goes northwards to the Plain of Esdraelon by way of one of the famous passes, either Megiddo or Dothan. In ancient times practically the whole of the country was well wooded, and until this day it has retained its name, Palestine, although the Philistines disappeared considerably over 2,000 years ago. The Philistines were a natural forest people, and their land was well described as the Land of Promise. Their wooded hills guarded fertile valleys, and the presence of sacred groves at the source of mountain springs is evidence that they had a natural regard for trees. Even in the days of the Jewish prophets, the country must have been well wooded, for were there not "lurking places for she-bears" which would come out and devour unruly children who were disrespectful?

In Byzantine days the country supported a population of about 3 million, and to-day Zionist authorities have estimated that the land might be made to provide homes for 2 to 4 millions above present population. The key to future prosperity lies in large scale reafforestation; until the hills are once again re-clothed, the valleys will not regain their former fertility. This fact is now generally recognized, and even under the rigours of World War I, Allenby initiated a planting campaign. This was further developed by the Men of the Trees in 1929, when many nurseries were started for the raising of young trees, and Arabs and Jews worked happily side by side to reclaim the land. An educational campaign was started through arbor days, and the Feast of the Trees became a nation-wide day of tree planting. There is no national conflict in planting, and many of the Jewish settlements have done splendid work. Malarial marshes have been planted with eucalyptus, or re-claimed for agriculture and citrus groves. Still more ambitious projects are planned for reclaiming areas of the Negeb. Some years ago, while visiting the Holy Land, I suggested that a canal be cut from Haifa to Tiberias, a very short distance as the crow flies. This would flood the Jordan Valley and, with some further excavations at the southern end, provide an inland water route to the Red Sea, Africa, and India. The cutting of this canal would increase precipitation along its route and assist the much-needed planting throughout the region. Now the latest suggestion is that a Jordan Valley Authority be set up to use the sweet waters of the Jordan to irrigate the belt of land on the west bank of this river and create a system of terraces on the steep slopes; at the same time to use the fall of the water to create cheap electric power. It is proposed that a portion of the Jordan should be carried westward in a tunnel to fertilize the plain of Esdraelon. It has been pointed out that this would interfere with the water supply of the Dead Sea, and so, to make up this loss, the salt water of the Mediterranean may be let in, and this fall of the water used to generate still more power. Whichever project is adopted, large-scale planting should follow. The Men of the Trees have led the way and have done much to educate public opinion as to forestry needs, but much remains to be done. At least 12,000 acres should be planted each year with 12 million trees. I estimate that the whole of Palestine might be reafforested at the cost of a single day of war. There is no country in the world that needs trees so urgently or would show greater response to planting than this land of promise.

One of the best-known trees of the North African evergreen belt is the Atlas Mountain cedar, *Cedrus atlantica*, and, in fact, the greatest distinction of the North African mountains is still the cedars, though few but battered veterans now remain where once great forests stood. Their enemies have been man, goats, and erosion. Along the seashore the tamarisk fixes the sand and often provides the first shelter; casuarinas, too, pine-like in appearance, add to the evergreen effect. Palms there are in plenty, and olive groves have their place in the foothills. But by far the best known cedar is that which grows in Lebanon, and these were made for ever famous by the Hebrew poet when he wrote:

> *The trees of the Lord are full of sap;*
> *The cedars of Lebanon, which He has planted;*
> *Where the birds make their nests.*

This beautiful tree is chiefly associated in our minds with lawns and parks, though it may become a valuable timber tree when grown silviculturally. After all, it was probably from this wood that King Solomon built his Temple. When excavating ancient cities with Sir Flinders Petrie in South Palestine, I was able to identify charred beams as cedar. The only indigenous forest of *Cedrus libani* is that of Lebanon, where about 400 trees still stand. In spite of ravages by goats and the demand for wood, these few veterans have survived the ages. Surely these historic trees should be protected and reinforced by further planting, and become a place of pilgrimage.

Cyprus is famous for another cedar cousin, *Cedrus brevifolia*, which was discovered in the mountains by Sir Samuel Baker in 1879, where they were growing at an altitude of 4,300 feet. The only other true cedar, *Cedrus Deodara*, is indigenous to the Himalayan Mountains.

Although the borders of the Mediterranean are the home of many of the evergreens, the trees readily adapt themselves to a great variety of climates and would welcome the hospitality of other countries.

Chapter Thirteen

THE WEALTH OF INDIA

In the wealth of the woods since the world began
The trees have offered their gifts to man.

Henry van Dyke.

TO REACH INDIA FROM THE EVERGREEN BELT, DESERTS AND waterless wastes must be traversed. These countries cradled civilization when their hills and plains were green with trees. The deserts of Iran and Mesopotamia tell the same story, first of gradual soil exhaustion and then of more rapid erosion. The mighty empires of Babylon, of Syria, Persia, and Carthage were destroyed by the advance of floods and deserts caused by the clearing of forests for agricultural land and by having their rivers drawn upon for additional supplies of water for irrigation. Their pristine fertility simply ran down under agriculture, worn out after long use. The ancient irrigation systems of Iraq have long been in decay, and the water-holding forests which fed their streams met the same fate as others in remote antiquity.

The traveller from the Mediterranean will encounter the great Iranian range, known to the ancients as the Zagros. These mountains sweep from the Caucasus in an almost unbroken curve, following roughly the line of the Turkish frontier and the Persian Gulf, until they fade away in the barren plains on the Baluchistan frontier, a distance of over 1,400 miles. Only here and there are wooded slopes, remnants of the ancient tree covering, but for the greater part the mountain scenery is bare and rugged with grey outcrops of slate forming part of a tangled mass of rock. Every kind of geological formation appears, as if thrown up by some cosmic upheaval. Permanent vegetation is rare, and in the rainless summer the rocks are hot and lifeless until they respond to the first rains in November by showing a faint green film, which by the spring has become a mass of luxuriant grass dotted with scarlet poppies and many other brightly-coloured flowers. By April the flora is scorched by the sun, and by May the rocks are once again bare. In July the temperature rises to the burning heat of 120°. When the forests of Iran are restored, the country will once again become a paradise on earth.

Even though much of Iran is desert, some parts have retained their beauty and fertility. There are still great valleys between the various ranges of the Kerman Mountains, which abound with the most rare and valuable forest products. Parts of the Provinces of Fars, Khuzistan, Ardeman, and Azerbaijan are rich with luxuriant vegetation, and the provinces of Gilan and Mazanderan, which lie between the Elburz and the Caspian Sea, enjoy woodland and water scenery. The mountainsides are clothed with trees and shrubs, while the plain, 300 miles long and from five to thirty miles wide, is dotted with mulberry plantations, vineyards, orchards, and orange groves.

Much mountainous country guards the western gate of India.

Forest exploitation has been responsible for much of the catastrophic erosion that scars the foothills of the Himalayas, and the human population of India, which is increasing at the rate of about 3 millions a year, makes ever further inroads upon India's forest wealth. The primeval forests, which once covered the country, are making their last stand in the hills and mountain systems. Even so, many of the hills have been deforested by reckless destruction during many generations, with the result that the climate and the water supply, upon which the very life of man depends, have deteriorated until desert conditions are met with in many an erstwhile fertile land. It was not until quite late on, under British rule, that conservation of India's forest wealth was contemplated. The British, like other nations, gained a foothold in India for trading purposes during the seventeenth century, but not before the middle of the nineteenth century did the forests come under administration. The name of B. H. Baden-Powell, at one time Conservator of the Punjab and acting Inspector-General of Forests during 1872–74, is closely connected with placing forest conservation on a sound basis; although as far back as 1856 a German forester from Hesse, Dietrich Brandis, was installed as superintendent of forests for Pegu, with wide powers, and was later entrusted with the organization of forest conservancy, with the result that to-day India is one of the bright exceptions to the indifference and neglect of forestry matters within the British Commonwealth.

The Indias, including Hindustan, Pakistan, Afghanistan, Burma, and Ceylon, with a total land area of 2,186,500 square miles and a population of 427,000,000 possesses a forest area of 486,304 square miles, or 22·2 per cent of the total land area. The Indian Empire contains every kind of elevation, climate, aspect, and soil, and its forests are among the richest and most varied in the world. This region contains at least 2,500 different species of trees. The old "British India", including Burma, comprises more than sixty per cent of the whole, the remainder being under the rule of the Indian States. In British territory the Government forests occupied an area of 251,572 square miles. These forests first became famous for teak and other valuable woods, which were exploited without thought for the future until the Indian Forest Service was brought into being. This Forest Service has now admittedly become one of the finest in the world, and has provided a model to other countries both within and without the British Commonwealth.

One of the first measures of the administration was to demarcate forest reserves. Suitable forest laws and codes had to be published for each area. Agreements were drawn up with the owners of the land, and under these settlements the lands were legally constituted as Government Forest Reserves. All questions relating to the customs, rights, and privileges of inhabitants had to be decided with due consideration. As soon as the forest reserves are properly constituted, silvicultural systems are introduced with a view to working them on a sustained-yield basis. Throughout the whole of once-British India, all forests capable of management to-day have their working plans, which are carried out as efficiently as in any forests in the world. Mr. D. Bourke-Borrowes, late of the Indian Forestry Service, recently described the great progress that had been made in India during the past century. The areas covered by plantations and afforestation now amount to several hundreds of thousand acres. The achievements accomplished in the work of reafforestation and land reclamation afford examples of great variety and magnitude. One of the early projects was started as far back as 1866, when the irrigated plantations in the Punjab were formed to provide an adequate supply of timber and fuel for the inhabitants of the bare plains. These plantations now comprise an area of about 60,000 acres. Where the forests had suffered from excessive grazing, producing widespread erosion, land reclamation and afforestation have been systematically carried out for many years past. One of the methods employed is to erect earthen dams across the ravines, and sow up the areas immediately behind such dams with suitable crops of trees. Much of the reclamation work in Central and Western India has consisted of reclothing bare and desiccated hill tracts situated in localities with very small rainfall. Such work is a slow and arduous undertaking.

It has been found by experience that where the indigenous vegetation can be maintained indefinitely, and at the same time be utilized economically, the problem of soil conservation ceases to exist. This is the aim of the Indian Forestry Service, and the object of sustained-yield forestry and controlled grazing. This system consists of managing a forest so that only as much wood is cut every season as is contained in the trees that would have died in the natural course of events, or where more is cut, the indigenous tree growth is correspondingly stimulated or reinforced by planting. Controlled grazing sees to it that the floral composition of the pastures does not materially change or, at any rate, does not deteriorate. Many of the methods to reclaim eroded land come within the scope of agriculture, where contour farming has proved to be advantageous in many cases. Shifting cultivation and uncontrolled clearing and burning are contributing factors to the enormous reduction of forest acreage.

The greatest forest-tree region is that of the western Himalayan Mountains, from the Indus to the Sardah River on the Nepal frontier. This is the realm of great conifers, outstanding among which is the Himalayan cedar, *Cedrus Deodara*, which thrives from 4,000 to 10,000 feet up, growing gregariously in association with spruce, blue pine, and three different kinds of oak. Sometimes the silver fir joins in with cypress, while yew is often found growing under its shade. At low elevations the

Dawn in the Pacific.

Among the Magic Islands.

deodar mixes with the long-leaved pine. Among other trees to
be found in the cedar forests are the birch, poplar, horse
chestnut, elm, hazel, hornbeam, maple, bird-cherry, walnut,
holly, box, and rhododendron, the latter sometimes growing to
almost tree height. The leaf fall of these nurse trees provides
rich humus for the cedars.

What do we know of the secret life of these magnificent
cedars which dominate the great mountain range from which
they have taken their name? How do they manage to reproduce
their kind and reign as princes in their forest paradise? How
have they come to rule the heights? Millions of years ago they
covered large tracts of the earth's surface, as may be proved by
examining the fossilized remains gathered by geologists from
the debris of their diggings. It is impossible to tell the difference
between the deodar and its cousin from the mountains of
Lebanon, or, indeed, from its other cousin which prefers the
Atlas Mountains. The wood at the heart of these trees looks the
same, and to all intents and purposes is the same. These
cousins differ only in form and foliage. In time of flood they
each migrated to the hills, where they survived by adapting
themselves to the conditions with which they had to contend.
The cedar of Lebanon and that of the Atlas Mountains had to
protect themselves against drying winds, and for that reason
they developed smaller leaves, so that they should not transpire
too much moisture. The Himalayan cedar had to contend
with the snows, and so he cunningly developed a drooping
character with longer leaves, which enabled him to shed the
snows without the risk of limb break. The male and female
flowers of the deodar are generally found on separate individuals, but this is not always so, and monoecious trees are
often met with by those who have carefully watched the business of pollinization. In October, at the end of the rainy season,
the young female cones expectantly open their scales, which,
when pollinated, close again. The cones hide their secret
through the following winter, when they increase but little in
size, but with the coming of spring growth becomes fast. By the
following October the cones are mature, and in November
they break up, discharging winged seeds, some of which may
find root in the weeds or moss of the forest floor.

I

Good seed years come irregularly, perhaps every three or four years. On the fringe of the forest, where the blue pine grows with the deodar, the young growth of both comes on together; but the blue pine grows faster, and may swamp the slower-growing deodar. The blue pine, *Pinus excelsa*, has from five to eight needles in a cluster, and cylindrical, soft-scaled cones. It looks like the Weymouth pine, but has much longer leaves and larger cones, and its bark, which is greyish-brown, is cut by shallow fissures into small, rather irregular plates. The flowers appear in the spring, and the cones ripen during the following autumn.

Lower down in the same mountain range are cedrelas, deciduous trees which grow at heights of up to 4,000 feet in the Punjab and eastwards, chiefly along streams. They are handsome trees with light, feathery foliage, and are rapid in growth. Their wood is durable and not eaten by white ants. It has a pleasing scent, and, in fact, is well known as the cigar-box cedar. Celtis is also found in these forests, and is planted around villages, where it is lopped for cattle fodder. The wood is tough and used for oars, tool handles, sticks, and wherever elasticity is required. Albizzia is another large deciduous tree. Siris is one of the best-known Indian trees, for it is not only very common in forests almost all over the country, but is cultivated in avenues and gardens. It is one of the fastest-growing trees, with beautiful, sweet-scented flowers. In contrast, *Olea*, the family of olives, is a slower-growing yet useful hill tree, chiefly found near villages and in valleys, partly in forests and partly on the borders of fields. It is prized by the villagers, and rarely cut down—though regularly lopped, so that it often has a rounded crown. The wood is valued for turning, for combs, agricultural implements, and fuel. In this region palms are scarce, but canes and wild dates are sometimes to be found. The more valuable of these forests are worked for the supply of Indian railways, while the wood of the pines is floated downstream to be used for building in the plains.

The chief trees of the dry region of the Punjab, Rajputana, Sind, and Baluchistan are species of acacia, prosopis, capparis, salvadora, tamarisk, and *Populus euphratica*; these are the *rukhs* of the Punjab. The most important species in the forests of

Baluchistan are *Juniperus macropoda*, *Pistacia*, and *Olea*. All these forests are worked to supply country needs.

The plains and sub-Himalayan tract of the north-western provinces, known as the United Provinces, are characterized by the presence of sal, *Shorea robusta*, a gregarious tree of great importance, which is found mixed with species of terminalia, lagerströmia, bombax, careya, schleichera, adina, eugenia, figs, and many others. The soil in which they grow is sandy gravel. Where the soil is deep and moist, sal disappears, and the mixed forest which takes its place includes albizzia, acacia, and dalbergia. Here too, is one of the world's most delicately scented woods, sissu, which is much sought after for making family chests.

Another important forest region lies in Central India, and includes the country lying south of the Jumna and north of the Godavery River, the Vindhia and Satpura Hills, as well as Orissa and the Circars on the east, and Khandesh and Guzerat on the west. This is the great deciduous, dry forest of India, which extends over the whole of the region, and passes north-wards into that previously described. All this region is also chiefly worked for country supply, except for teak and sal, used on the railways. In the western part, teak is the chief tree, while sal dominates the eastern part. There are many other genera and some bamboos. In ravines, palms and tree-ferns are sometimes found growing with wild mango.

The eastern Himalaya is a vast region with a great variety of forest trees. In the higher slopes are many firs, spruce, larch, yew, juniper, and hemlock spruce. These range downwards until they reach the zone of the rhododendrons, which are mixed with oaks and chestnuts, while lower still are great maples, magnolias, and other less-known species. Still farther down appear large trees of cedrela, terminalia, with palms and large screw-pines, *Pandanus furcatus*, and these once again pass into sal forests, with the addition of *Schima Wallichii* and *Dillenia*.

The forests of the Khasia Hills are well known for their many species of oak. Passing southwards from northern Bengal, the Assam Valley, and Khasia Hills, is a great forest region which extends from the valley of Cachar, southwards down the

Lushai Hills, to the border of Arrakan and eastwards to the
boundaries of Burma. In this great forest are giant trees on
deep, rich alluvial lands and along rivers, and smaller growth
with dense masses of bamboo on the hills. In the Chittagong
Forest are the dipterocarpus trees. They are truly magnificent,
towering to a height of 150 to 200 feet, mounting over the other
forest denizens, which themselves form a second tier but a little
way below their superiors. The wealth of this tree is exploited
by the villagers, who tap it for its oil. A single tree may yield
as much as 7 lb. of oil each night. This is sought after for
making torches, and that amount would be sufficient to make a
hundred torches or paint a small house or a boat. It is at night
that the Indian goes into the forest to collect this treasured oil.
He makes a hole at breast height or about 4 feet above the root
of the tree, and in it lights a few dried leaves every third
evening. The wood of this great tree is used in house-building
and for dugout canoes; logs from 40 to 60 feet in length are
often dragged out of the forest.

There are two other forest regions, that of the southern part of
the Deccan plateau, the slopes of the plateau on the east and
south, and the Carnatic country. These forests are deciduous,
but with more teak than is found elsewhere, and sal disappears.
Among the species particularly noted are the sandal tree,
which will grow on half-bare, stony forest lands. Here, too, are
ebony and satinwood. In this region are large tracts covered
with the Palmyra palm, one of the most useful of Indian
plants, for its strong tough outside wood is valuable in house-
building, and its leaves and fruit provide valuable products.

In the last region come the forests of the mountain range of
the Western Ghats with the lands between their foothills and
the sea. In some places there are dry areas with growth not
unlike that of the deciduous forest of Central India, with a good
deal of teak, though the greater part consists of hill forests on
lower hill slopes, evergreen in character, and here teak is the
dominant tree.

Burma is the main home of this world-famous timber tree,
Tectona grandis as it is called. For a century or more the wealth
of its forests has been exploited by governments and conces-
sionaires. The trees are girdled while still standing; thus they

"This king of forest trees"—Kauri pine, North Auckland.

"Much of the Southern Alps is in the eternal snows"—the fern track to Franz Josef Glacier, South Island, New Zealand.

are killed and partly seasoned before they are laid low. When
they fall to earth they often bring with them a shower of debris
and creepers by which they had been attached to their neighbours. Next they are cross-cut into logs of convenient length,
and teams of elephants are used to extract them from their
jungle home. Great is the sagacity of the Burmese elephant,
who will guide the log along a difficult trail and eventually
bring it to the desired destination. It is fascinating to watch a
big elephant pick up a log, carefully balancing it on his tusks
and manœuvring it between the tall stems of standing trees.
The large logs are dragged to the nearest floating river, and
pushed over its bank. On striking the water, they are carried
downstream to the rafting point. As they pass into the main
current, skilled Burmese loggers spring from the bank and ride
the logs to their destined place to form the huge raft in which
they will find their way down the great river to the sea.

Modern man is making increasing demands on the wealth of
these mighty forests—these forests which contain a greater
variety of trees than any others in the world. There is abundance for all, if they are wisely exploited and worked on a
sustained-yield basis.

Chapter Fourteen

THE TRAGEDY OF CHINA .

When the forests go, the waters go, the fish and game go,
crops go, herds and flocks go, fertility departs. Then the age-
old phantoms appear, stealthily one after another—Flood,
Drought, Fire, Famine, Pestilence.

Robert Chambers.

THE GOOD EARTH FROM WHICH MAN SPRANG, THE GENTLE mother that bore him from her womb, must be tended with loving care; otherwise she will not support him. The body of Earth must have her green covering of trees or other plants. Her skin is sensitive to the behaviour of man, who has never quite mastered the art of continuous cultivation of land which was once covered with forest. The folly of exposing her nakedness has been shown graphically in China. Deserts now reign in the very birthplace of ancient civilization. The great north-west loessial region now resembles a huge battlefield, scarred and denuded. That fertile soil, which when touched by rain, will bear crops two or three times a year, easily dissipates itself unless covered by trees or grasses.

The name "loess" is adopted from that of a Tertiary deposit which appears in the Rhine Valley. It is a brownish-coloured earth, extremely porous, crumbles easily between the fingers, and readily forms clouds of dust. The wind-blown loess is one of the richest soil materials known, and its qualities are similar to that which has formed the black soils of the Russian steppes. In the Province of Shansi, loess often covers the subsoil to a great depth and is extremely sensitive to erosion, which will cut it into deep clefts, making travelling across its surface impossible. Over vast areas, where once the soil was deep and fertile, little remains but gaping chasms, sometimes hundreds of feet wide and deep. The eroded material has been spread on the valleys and plains, and has found its way to the rivers and sea. The Yellow River and the Yellow Sea are named from the colour of the eroded soil which has been lost to the hinterland. So great has the erosion been that often the beds of the rivers are raised, like that of the Mississippi, until they are higher than the surrounding country. The waters tear down the hill-sides in ever-increasing torrents and in China create the most disastrous floods that the world has seen. It has been estimated that the Yellow River alone transports an annual load of 2,500 million tons of soil. There are other regions where rapid erosion is taking place, but the Yellow River has been described as the outstanding and eternal symbol of the mortality of civilization.

Constant farming has gradually exhausted these soils, and, in spite of a vast system of terraces which has been built up in an attempt to check erosion, the destructive forces have not been kept in control, but have devastated the loess region to the north and threatened both the soil of the plains and the lives of 100 million people who inhabit them. Untold human suffering has resulted from the periodic floods of the Yellow River. Millions have died of starvation after their crops have been washed away. The Chinese farmers have been helpless in the face of the destructive force which they and their forebears have in their ignorance let loose upon themselves. If only former generations had treated their hill forests with due respect, this great catastrophe might have been averted, but they failed to realize their dependence upon the green covering of their hills.

In the past, conservationists have pointed to China as pro-viding the classic example of the evils of de-afforestation. It was plain that her denuded mountains were the direct cause of devastating floods and famine. But in fairness to China it should be remembered that the disintegration was slow, and, bad as the position is to-day, China still manages to maintain a vast population, whereas other civilizations, such as those of the Babylonian Empire and Carthage, have vanished altogether. In Ceylon, Central America, and other tropical regions may be seen evidences of bygone civilizations which grew upon ex-ploitation of the forests. But the jungle tide returned and ex-terminated the invaders, who had not learnt the art of wooing their tricky soils.

So remote are these happenings of bygone ages that they

seem unreal in these days of so-called advanced civilization. We are inclined to flatter ourselves that we can control Nature. It is thought that science and chemistry, with technical knowledge, have advanced to such a degree that they will solve all our problems. It therefore comes as rather a shock to us that the civilizations of the New World, which have developed with such rapidity, may decline with like speed. Nature is still our ruler, and if we attempt to outwit or restrain her, or to transgress her laws, her answer is sterile fields and empty granaries. When we come to know this truth we shall be humbled and less inclined to point the accusing finger at China, and realize that we have all made the same mistakes. We shall have a great longing to remedy our shortcomings. It may occur to us that the present agricultural systems and methods of land exploitation, which have brought such disaster, are a modern symptom of maladjustment between man and his environment. In all humbleness and in the spirit of earnest research, we may approach the problems of China and learn from her mistakes how best to tackle the colossal tasks that to-day lie before the whole world.

Among the thoughtful people in China to-day there is a growing desire to make use of the up-to-date knowledge relating to soil conservation. China is a nation of small farmers, their average holding being no more than 4 acres. In the valleys and on the alluvial plains intensive agriculture produces rice, sugar cane, bananas, citrus fruits, and many vegetables. Hillside terracing is the common practice in many parts. This entails great labour with meagre returns. The sub-tropical climate of the south produces luxuriant growth both on the coast and in the interior, although in the populated areas most of the hills have long been bared of their tree covering. Here and there, however, may still be seen little ragged specimens of pines and other trees, with clumps of bamboo, poor remains of once luxuriant forests. For the greater part, rank grasses grow and provide rough grazing for the water-buffalo. From time to time this grass is fired and burns any tree or shrub that may be struggling to regenerate its species. If a peasant farmer is asked why he burns the hillside, he may say that it is to scare away snakes and tigers, or to provide ash to fertilize the rice fields below. But the fires burn away the top soil and what little humus there may be, and lay bare the mineral soil, which is unproductive and easily eroded.

It must not be imagined that China is without forests. On the average every Chinese, whether he knows it or not, has nearly ½ acre of forest. In many of the densely-populated agricultural sections there is actually no timber for the average Chinese. His house may be built of native clay, and often his fuel is the dung of native cattle. Even so, when he dies he must have a coffin made of wood. Ordinary coffins are made of thick planks, but the wealthy have them hewn from a single log and lacquered in black. Wood for coffins has, in fact, been one of the heaviest drains on the Chinese forests.

Camphor wood is one of the most prized trees, and fine specimens may still be found growing in association with Oriental gum and many species of leguminous trees, and with the laurel and fir families. These frequently grow on the higher slopes in mixture with native pine and Chinese fir. Bamboo is of great economic importance, because the Chinese are most clever in putting this to a variety of uses, from food to baskets or carrying-poles. Freshly germinated seeds of the bamboo form an important part of Chinese meals, and often in time of famine, as in India, the bamboos seed themselves gregariously over considerable areas, and in this way, when other food is scarce, Nature comes to the rescue and provides the delicious bamboo shoots to stave off hunger.

There are more hardwoods than softwoods, and that may help to account for the fact that China has managed to survive. It has been estimated that there are 170,000 square miles of hardwoods in the country, whereas 140,000 square miles have been classed as coniferous forest, though this by no means consists of pure coniferous stands. The total forest area of the country is 310,000 square miles, or about seven per cent of the total land area. Of this, half is classed as marketable and the other half inaccessible.

Many are the varieties of trees grown in the forests. One of the most common and most valuable is the Chinese fir, *Abies fargesii*. It is a tall tree, from 80 to 120 feet high, and at one time these trees were found up to 4 feet in diameter. The more tropical broad-leaved evergreens give place in part to deciduous northern types where altitude affects the climate. For instance, on the upper slopes of the Mei Ling are found many trees and plants typical of temperate regions, such as oak, hornbeam, birch, and maple. Broad-leaved evergreen trees grow in the more sheltered ravines, together with bamboo and many varieties of shrubs and woody lianas. Few large trees remain, but there is plenty of evidence that the forests of the hills have been exploited and burnt over in the past, and the dense vegetation indicates how forest cover would quickly rehabilitate the hills. In many parts the annual precipitation is as high as 70 inches a year, and, if the hills were protected from human interference, the forest cover would return.

It is essential to define land use clearly, and to keep the hills, which are the natural domain of trees, under forest types. That alone will prevent the kind of erosion which is particularly noticeable where crop cultivation has been pushed up steep hillsides. Forests will, moreover, reduce flood areas in times of heavy rains and hold back the rushing waters which carry such great quantities of good earth into the rivers, filling up the channels and blocking navigation, as well as ruining the farms and threatening human life.

Progressive fire protection, and policing to prevent fires, would in time result in the return of the forests, at least in the warm sub-tropical regions; but the work of restoration would be speeded up by wholesale planting and the inauguration of large-scale re-afforestation. Often the will to plant is there, as is evidenced by many little groves of pine trees planted by native farmers, but so great is the need for fuel that they are often sacrificed before they are many years old. Ordinary fuel wood is desperately needed in China. Charcoal-burners have made inroads into the rapidly diminishing supplies of wood, and denudation proceeds apace, with disastrous effects upon agriculture. The tide of destruction must be turned; seedlings must be planted by the millions on all denuded sites. The broad-leaved species must be encouraged as soil-improvers, and an evergreen covering be maintained by the planting of such trees as China pine, which later on can be underplanted with Chinese fir as a half-shade-bearer. Any leguminous trees that will thrive should be introduced to impregnate the ground with nitrogen. Ipil-ipil, *Leucaena glauca*, a fast-growing leguminous tree successfully established in the Philippines, might well be tried in the tropical and sub-tropical regions of southern China, as also acacia, *Albanesia stipulata*, which has been grown with such good results in some of the tea plantations of Nyasaland. The root system of this acacia brings up valuable fertilizing material from the subsoil, to be incorporated in the leaves which fall to the ground, thus preserving moisture and enriching the surface soil. Tree crops such as persimmon and tung oil may be planted where climate and soil permit. Nut and fruit production might well be used as a catch crop when growing forests for timber, and they would reimburse the native cultivator during the years of waiting for the timber crop. It is my belief that, as a first step, an intensive educational campaign must be launched, with experimental and demonstration plantations throughout the country. The farmer must be shown that it is not profitable to attempt to grow food crops, such as rice, on steep hillsides, which are the natural domain of forests.

The Chinese farmer is a great individualist, and often he does little more than supply his own needs from his small-holding. This is often scattered in small parcels, so that he spends much of his time in walking from plot to plot. His intense love of the land and individual pride in land-ownership rules out the feasibility of collective farming, as it is practised in Russia. Moreover, the Chinese will not sell his land on any scale large enough to allow individual owners to control and operate large tracks on rational lines. In practice it is found that ownership tends towards smaller areas, as the farms are passed on to the sons of present owners. It has been suggested that much might be done by exchange of land, but this process is slow and, even when the total land area is gathered into one parcel, it may be too small to be an effective economic unit. Part of the solution may be to encourage co-operative farming side by side with community-owned forests.

The mountainous country of Korea, which was annexed by Japan early in this century, provided one of the outstanding examples of forest denudation. Originally much of this country was doubtless well-wooded, as is evidenced by the remaining woodlands, which contain a great variety of species including pines, fir, oak, maple, limes, and birch. Juniper, mountain ash, and walnut are also found, together with Spanish chestnut, hazel, hornbeam, wild plum, pear, and willow.

As were other parts of the then Chinese Empire, through centuries of bad government and misrule, together with the constant pressure of increasing population, the country was stripped of practically all its forests. When the Japanese took it over and re-named it Chosen, after an ancient name meaning "morning calm", much of the soil subject to heavy erosion had been washed into the adjacent valleys. Many of the streams had dried up, often making the cultivation of rice impossible. To-day a veritable transformation may be seen, for new forests are coming on and many of the hillsides, unsuited to farming, are clothed with a new green mantle. Already there has been real improvement in the supply of water for rice paddies, and much of the erosion on the little farms has been checked. As early as 1907 the Japanese Residency-General had induced the Korean Government to undertake afforestation work, and in 1911 new forestry regulations were issued. In the same year the Governor-General established an Arbor Day, and soon thousands of millions of seedlings were being planted for the purpose of re-establishing the Korean forests. The Government further encouraged the formation of forestry associations, and within twenty years there were as many as 350, with a total membership of nearly one million.

Very soon there was a special Government office controlling the State forests, covering between 5 and 6 million acres in the basins of the Yalu and the Tumen, and engaging in various kinds of work tending not only to improve the forests themselves, but to improve their indirect utilization. The principal trees in the forests are similar to those found in the frigid zone, such as larch, fir, birch, and aspen. Seedlings of the most suitable varieties for this region were raised in special nurseries.

The total area of forest lands in Chosen amounts to about 39 million acres, or seventy-one per cent of the total area of the Peninsula; but, as it has long been neglected, the area of standing forests is estimated at about 13 million acres only, and

"The Silence of a hundred centuries"—Puraroto caves, North Island, New Zealand.

"The dignity of the mighty forests"—road cut through virgin forest,
South Island, New Zealand.

these are mostly found in the remote north and in the eastern highlands. Of the remaining area, about 18 million acres are covered with young trees, and about 7 million acres are entirely bare. Formosa, returned to China in 1945, is treated on page 146.

The real problem in such regions of abandoned land is not always immediate reafforestation, but soil-building, for that must precede the productive forest. The rebuilding of a forest soil involves soil surface phenomena. When there is insufficient litter cover, it is not porous enough to be capable of absorbing rain. As the north and south of the peninsula differ widely in climate, there is scope for the use of many varieties of trees. In the basins of the Oryoku and the Tumen in the north, and on the higher mountains, the fir, larch, and Korean pine flourish with birch, and in the central and upper southern part the Japanese red and black pine, deciduous and evergreen oak, together with alder, are the main constituents. In the lower southern part oak and bamboo are in great evidence. The fact that there are as many as 700 varieties of useful trees in Chosen shows how well it is suited for afforestation on the widest possible scale. In recent years afforestation of hillsides and waste lands has been taken up to prevent sand-drifts and to afford a future supply of timber. This work has for the most part fallen to the Lumber Undertaking Station and the branch offices of the Forestry Section, and the area so covered totals over 15,000 acres. Plantations maintained by public bodies have made great progress, and reafforestation has been undertaken by individual enterprise and development companies, many of which have started their own nurseries on a large scale.

There are many local industries which have arisen out of the forests. These are often on quite a small scale, but none the less valuable for that. Sometimes Chinese girls may be seen standing barefooted in the water of a small swiftly-flowing stream, their voluminous white muslin dresses gathered up around their waists, washing a yellowish-white batch of raw paper-pulp swung backwards and forwards in a cotton sheet in the stream. The paper-pulp mill may be nothing more than a broken-down shanty with wooden tanks and vats, without any power machinery. Nevertheless, from such enterprise are produced valuable hand-made papers which would favourably compete in quality with anything made in the great paper mills of Europe and the West.

Even though Western civilizations may regard such methods as out-of-date, the fact remains that China still produces quality, and her slower methods have eked out her resources. But for these so-called backward methods of industry, China, the oldest civilization in the world of to-day, could not have survived; so let us not regard her tragedy as one that cannot be redeemed, for is not modern greed and speed hastening a far greater tragedy in a much shorter time?

Chapter Fifteen

THE MIRACLE OF JAPAN

Trees for fruitage and fire and shade
Trees for the cunning builders' trade.

.   .   .   .   .

He made them of every grain and girth,
For the use of man in the Garden of Earth.

⸱ Bliss Carmen.

T HE JAPANESE ARE A PEOPLE WHO HAVE AN INHERENT LOVE for trees, and it has helped them in their struggle to save the land surface of their islands, which, but for the well-tended forests, might have eroded away and suffered the same fate as Atlantis and the continent of Mu. The fact that Nature endowed the islands with so varied a covering assisted the inhabitants to preserve them. It is a miracle, indeed, that these islands have survived so many volcanic upheavals and that their forests have contrived to prevent catastrophic erosion which would have inevitably doomed them to destruction.

It is well known that the difference in the geological strata causes variations in the soil both in kind and nature, and considerably affects the growth of forest trees and the formation of forests. For instance, the more primitive coniferous forests cover an extensive area, where they retain their virgin appearance, grown by natural regeneration on the strata of igneous rocks, while the greater part of the forests which have been planted are on the aqueous rocks and sandstone. The basic strata of Japan consists of rocks of archaean formation upon which the other strata have been deposited. The volcanic eruptions in each geologic period have extended over the surface. There are large varieties of rocks belonging to the Tertiary and Quarternary, but the largest area is occupied by andesite and basalt.

Japan's topography and climate not only affect the species of forest trees, but the condition of their growth and the composition of the forests. Extending as the country does through nearly 30° of latitude, it is natural that it should provide climatic conditions for a wide range of species. Five thousand have been named, and of these nearly 300 are similar to those grown in the British Isles. There are as many as 600 species of forest trees, of which scores occupy an important position in forest economy. As much as sixty-three per cent of the total land area is classified as forest and comprises about 59 million acres. Not all of this is productive, for in the course of Japan's industrial revolution nearly 7 million acres of her forests suffered devastation through improper use and by fire. The march of Western civilization introduced new desires and industries. Japanese foresters all seem to be agreed that the political revolution in the beginning of the Meiji Era (1868) produced a disastrous effect upon the preservation of the forests. It appears that throughout the country they were mercilessly cut down so that in all quarters of Japan hills and mountains were deprived of trees. The consequence was that not only was the economy of the forests jeopardized, but the economy of the people at large was deranged, for heavy blows were dealt to productive industry in all spheres on account of the annual inundations which devastated many parts of the country. This state of affairs was particularly noticeable in the forest districts with granite strata, such as in the provinces Omi, Mino, and those portions of the Chu-gok facing the Inland Sea. The adjustment and improvement of these denuded lands called for immediate attention, and it is to the credit of the Government in 1875 that Regulations for the Provisionary Investigation of State Forests were published. The extent of the denuded land was thus made known, and in 1877 at Nishiga-hava, Tokyo, the forest experimental station was established for the purpose of carrying out experiments regarding the cultivation of trees.

There followed a series of progressive forestry measures which became more and more effective, and have resulted in firmly establishing a system whereby the forests have increasingly benefited and the tide of destruction been turned. Timber was soon in demand for railway sleepers, telegraph poles, and pit-props, while ever-increasing quantities had to be supplied for paper pulp and a hundred and one other purposes. Nevertheless, the present total volume of standing timber has been

"Ruthless destruction of the forest began"—felling a big tree in the Karri forests of Western Australia.

"There still r
main whole fore
in their primiti
state" — Nor
Queensland.

Baobab tree,
North-Western
Australia.

estimated by Japanese foresters to be about 67 billion cubic feet, of which 32 billion feet are softwoods and 35 billion feet hardwoods. The estimated annual timber and pulpwood increment is in the neighbourhood of 685 million cubic feet. Systematic forest conservation has been followed with good results for many centuries, and the Japanese were among the first to plant trees on a large scale. The land lends itself to extensive afforestation, and only one-fifth of the whole land area is suited for farm crops. But during World War II many of the hillsides were cleared to grow food, and extensive mulberry groves, the source of the great silk industry, have been sacrificed to meet the demand for more food to feed the 72 million people. The average size of a farm is a little more than 1 acre, and nearly half the population is engaged in farming. Land which will grow crops is so valuable that many of the farms are cropped three times a year. Fertility is maintained by the thrifty use of "night soil". This precious human excretion is collected each evening, in low wooden buckets on wagons drawn by horses or oxen, from the cities where people are fed with the produce grown for them by the hard-working farmers. The new farms made where the trees had been freshly cleared had an accumulation of humus, and this helped to solve the food problems. Moreover, food supplies came from the standing forests in the shape of wild game, acorns, nuts and other fruits, mushrooms of many kinds, and bamboo shoots. For instance, in 1945 over a million tons of acorns were collected by children to be used in the manufacture of flour. The indirect benefit of the forests cannot be calculated in a country where the very existence of farmland is dependent on the forest for protection. So rugged is the topography and steep the mountainsides that, but for the forest cover, erosion would be rapid, for in regions of excessive rainfall and winds of high velocity the soil would wash away and be lost, while farmlands would be destroyed by floods and be inundated by debris. But, thanks to the long-term forestry practised by the Japanese people, vast stretches of unbroken forest mantle the upper slopes of the mountain ranges. When areas have been clear cut, as a rule they have at once been reafforested, over 10 million acres having been planted in the last fifty years. The

K

forests are classed as "utilization forests" and "protective forests". The object of the latter is to preserve the safety of the land and further the welfare of the people by licensing the felling of trees. In the "utilization forests", systematic felling and replanting takes place to provide the necessary timber for houses and the needs of industry. Felling methods might be regarded as primitive by Western landowners, but nothing is wasted; trees are felled close to the ground and converted in little saw-mills, of which there are between 7,000 and 8,000. Both circular saws and band saws are employed in these, and it is quite common to find logs with a diameter of only a few inches and 6 feet long being converted into planks.

The forests of Japan cover the whole range of climates from the torrid forest zone to that of the frigid. The torrid forests are those of the whole of Formosa, or Taiwan, the southern half of the Luchu Islands, Yaeyama, and the Bohnine Islands. Here may be found the Ako or wild fig, *Ficus Wightiana*, variety japonica, Tako-no-ki, *Pandanus odratissimus*, ryugan, *Nephelium longana*, binroji, *Areca catechu*, tsugu, *Arenga saccharifera*, basho, *Musa basjoo*, and bamboos which grow vigorously everywhere to a great size. Their strength and quality make them much sought after for use in furniture-making and buildings.

The tropical forest zone comprises Shikoku and Kyushu, as well as the northern part of the Luchu Islands, covering the southern part of Honshu south of 36° north latitude. Great are the number of varieties of trees in this zone, and they possess considerable value in the economy of the forest. As a result of the reckless felling of trees in the past there are very few forests which retain their primitive features. In Honshu, virgin forests are found only in the neighbourhood of shrines and temples.

The most important among the broad-leaved trees is the Kusu-no-ki, *Cinnamomum camphora*, which forms extensive natural forests. It is not particular as to soils, and thrives almost anywhere with protection from cold winds. This valuable camphor tree grows in Formosa up to 3,000 feet above sea level, forming pure or mixed forest with other species. The wood is hard and lustrous, retaining a peculiar fragrance, and is prized in the making of costly furniture. It is most durable and is valued for ship-building. The great demand for camphor has encouraged the people to make plantations of it, and millions of seedlings have been distributed to encourage this enterprise.

It is not always the large trees that are the most valuable. Tsuge, the box tree, *Buxus sempervirens*, variety japonica, hardly ever attains more than about 18 inches in diameter or 50 feet in height, but the hard, uniform nature of the wood, with annual rings hardly distinguishable, is prized most of all as the material for fine carving and sculpture. This tree thrives in a limestone soil and may be generated from seed or cuttings. There are several oaks in this zone, including ichii-gashi, *Quercus gilva*, shira-gashi, *Quercus vibrayeana*, and aka-gashi, *Quercus acuta*. Of all the broad-leaved trees these three varieties are most extensively utilized, for they provide the handles of agricultural implements, and are used for building railway trucks and coaches, as well as farm carts and wagons and rudders of boats. The wood from ichii-gashi was valued from ancient times for supplying the best material for spear handles, and felling was strictly controlled by the Government. The principal deciduous oaks are kunugi, *Quercus serrate*, and konara, *Quercus glandulifera*. Both these are used for fuel and charcoal, and they are grown extensively for this purpose.

The most important coniferous forests consists of *Pinus densiflora* and *Pinus thunbergii*. The former grows thickly everywhere, from the southern extremity of Kyushu to the southern part of Hokkaido, with the exception of marshy places. It will thrive in clay or clayish soil or on dry land at high altitudes up to 6,000 feet above sea level. It is one of the light-demanders, is easy to plant, and is therefore extensively used in re-afforestation, where it is often grown in mixture with bamboo and konara, *Quercus glandulifera*. Because of its hardy nature and rapid growth, it is often chosen by public bodies, temples, and shrines, as well as by private individuals. The wood is light-reddish in colour, hard and elastic. It is rich in resin, and is durable in moisture and sought after for engineering and pit-props. It is second only to sugi, *Cryptomeria japonica*, as a building material, and is indispensable as a fuel and particularly popular with night fishermen, who use it for torches to decoy the fish. Moreover, one of the most popular mushrooms thrives among forests of this pine, which can be grown on poor sand almost down to the seashore, where it will stand up to the full blast of sea breezes and tolerate salt spray. In a similar way *Pinus thunbergii* has many popular uses, and its rich resin content enables it to withstand exposure for many years. It is well suited to bridge-building and various engineering works. As a fuel it is very combustible.

Besides these trees, there are bamboos, among the most useful of all the forest growths of Japan. They are cultivated in the private forests everywhere in this country, but chiefly in the southern part of Honshu, Shikoku, and Kyushu. These bamboos grow to enormous height at great speed; they will often attain 60 or 70 feet in a few months. Of all the bamboos, *Phyllostachys mitis* makes the most rapid growth, for it sometimes reaches 1 foot in diameter and 85 feet in height.

The Temperate Forest Zone ranges from the northern half of Honshu to the southern half of Hokkaido, or from 36° to 43° north latitude, and the average temperature is about 50° F. This is not only the most valuable but the most beautiful forest region of Japan. There are over sixty varieties of forest trees in this zone, among them the famous Japanese cedars, five of which are the most outstanding—namely, hinoki, sawara, kayamaki, hiba, and nezuki. *Chamaecyparis obtusa* is the most highly-prized, and it enters more into temple construction than any of the others. The great forests of hinoki are in the mountains of Kiso, near the centre of Honda, the largest island. The natural growth of this tree of the Imperial Forests of Kiso is famous, and the forest is one of the three most beautiful in the whole of Japan. Hinoki thrives best at a height of from 1,600 to 4,500 feet above sea level, but it will grow above or below these ranges so long as there is sufficient atmospheric moisture. It will grow either alone or mixed with other species, where it always retains its most attractive silvicultural characteristics. This beautiful cedar grows to a height of 130 feet with a diameter of four feet. It has horizontal branches which form a pyramidal crown, rather like its cousin, Lawson's cypress, of the other coast of the Pacific. Its trunk is picturesque with its deep-furrowed or scaly bark. The branches are closely set with scale-like leaves. Altogether it is a remarkably graceful tree and is particularly beautiful in its own forest setting. The wood is dense and compact, white or slightly yellowish in colour, without prominent grain. It has a peculiar flavour which probably protects it against attack from insects. It has good working qualities and, when worked by Japanese craftsmen, takes on a satin finish, which makes it the most popular timber amongst wood-workers. It is used also for bridges and shipbuilding, and, above all, it is noted for its great durability. It is stated that there are some Japanese temples where hinoki is found in good condition after twelve or thirteen centuries. Hinoki was used at Ise for the building of the sacred Shinto shrines, which are a classic example of pure Japanese architecture, uninfluenced by Buddhism and the Chinese School.

So many are the beautiful conifers of the temperate forest zone, all with some peculiar or especially excellent quality, that space will not permit their classification. Their musical names are as beautiful as their forms, and remind one of the Maori names of the New Zealand trees. There is the hiba, *Thujopsis dolabrata*, which grows at high altitudes very slowly, the wood being white and rather like hinoki, while yet another arboristane, nezuki, is dark-reddish. Koyamaki, *Sciadotytis verticillata*, sometimes known to Westerners as umbrella pine because of its umbrella-shaped crown, intrigues botanists because it is an outstanding example of a conifer with two forms of leaves. There are the scale-like leaves, which are scattered thickly along the shoots and at the ends of the branches, and in the axils of these are clusters of from eight to twenty-five flat leaves from 3 to 6 inches in length. At first acquaintance, it is a puzzle to say whether it is a pine, cedar, or cypress.

Sawara, a cousin of hinoki, which among botanists is known as *Chamaecyparis pisifera*, and koyamaki grow together or mixed with other species at from 2,700 to 5,400 feet above sea level in such provinces as Yanato, Bungo, Sabsuua, Omi, Shimotsaki, and Uzen. Sawara is a light-reddish wood which is much used for carved panels in house partitions. Moni is a true fir, *Abies firma*; it loves shady places and has the peculiarity of growing much more rapidly during the latter portion of its life. The wood is light and soft, easily warping and pliable, but it finds its use for pulping.

There are many other strange and beautiful-sounding names,

such as himeko-matsu, goyo-matsu, bara-momi, and kara-matsu. The last is none other than the well-known Japanese larch, *Larix leptolepsis*. Natural forests of this species are found on the slopes of the mountains of Euji and Asama and in the Azumi county of Shinano province. This valuable tree grows on dry soil of volcanic strata, making healthy growth in the strongest sunlight, and is intolerant of shade. It will grow rapidly on the poorest of soils, and it is now being widely planted to provide timber for houses, ships, telegraph poles, and engineering works. In this Zone there are many varieties of deciduous broad-leaved trees, which occupy the greater part of the forest area, though they are seldom found in pure stands. The name "konara" sounds almost Irish. It is a lovely name and is the Japanese for the beautiful oak *Quercus glandulifera*. Kashiwa is another valuable oak, so is onara. Kaba is a birch and doro-no-ki is the well-known balsam poplar. All these grow in mixture in many parts, whereas han-no-ki is the Japanese alder, which chooses swampy places. Buna, the beech, forms pure single-aged forests which extend over Honshu and the southern half of Hokkaido. It is interesting that other varieties of broad-leaved trees grow irregularly mixed with numerous kinds of broad-leaved trees and conifers, whereas buna will grow in pure stands, the reason being that beech is a shade-bearer and will thrive under other trees, eventually taking possession of the soil, because the seedlings of the other broad-leaved trees do not have a chance to survive under the dense canopy of the beech. And yet, in spite of this, beech is recommended as a soil-improver to foster the growth of other species, such as oak. At first thought it sounds paradoxical, but in practice the trees of the other species, if liable to be outgrown by the beech, are planted as many as twenty years in advance. At the end of this time lines are cut at right angles to the original rows and it is along these cleared lines that the beech are planted. The side shade provided will stimulate their growth, and up to the hundredth year there should be little risk of the beech suppressing the other species. At that stage, however, many of the beech may be tending to annihilate their neighbours, and they should be removed. The spaces thus opened out will give an opportunity for young beech to germinate and fill the gaps that have been made by the removal of their parent trees. The second generation of beech will continue the work of providing ground cover and soil improvement, and in another hundred years may themselves be removed to give place to yet another generation of their kind.

Yachidamo, reminiscent of the Scandinavian world tree, yggdrasil, also of an ash, *Fraxinus mandshurica*, is a tree which is grown extensively and, with katsura, may be seen all over Hokkaido. The wood of this tree has the valuable qualities of durability as well as elasticity. Inu-enju is another broad-leaved tree which grows in the northern part of Honshu and in south Hokkaido. This wood possesses a peculiar and beautiful lustre, and is greatly valued for buildings and decorative purposes. Kurumi, one of the walnuts, likes the fertile soil of the lower land among the mountains in the central as well as the northern part of Honshu. In the plains of Ishikari, Tokachi, and Hokkaido there are beautiful forests of this walnut tree, where it grows with yachidamo, katsura, and nire, the elm. In Japan, as in the U.S.A. and Europe, the first use of the walnut is for rifle stocks, but it would be valuable for decorative panelling anywhere, and it will make excellent veneers or plywood. The wood of hari-giri, on the other hand, is white in colour, and yet it is also in demand for decoration as well as for implements. In deep forests of fertile land it grows to a huge size. Kashiwa and onara are two oaks which like the wet mountain places in the north-eastern districts of Honshu, but they will also thrive in the plains of Hokkaido, where they form pure forests of oak. Kuri is the common Spanish chestnut, which is also a native of Kyushu, Shikoku, and the western part of Honshu, and it is beloved by the people of Japan for the beauty of its forests on the slopes of high mountains, where it grows in association with buna, the beech, hiba, that lovely thuya, kiwada, katsura, and also sawa-gurumi. Such deciduous, broad-leaved trees as tochi-no-ki, a kind of horse chestnut, nire, the elm, and han-no-ki, the alder, toneriko, the ash, saikachi, enoki, and yanagi, the weeping willow, are not used in the formation of forests but are valued for the purpose of creating beautiful protective belts.

Hako-yanagi, *Populus tremula*, and doro-no-ki, the balsam

poplar, love moist, light soils and sunny positions, and thrive wherever they find these conditions. In the Monbetsu and Shari counties of Kitami province, in the Kamikawa county of Ishikari province, and in the Tokachi county of Tokachi Province in Hokkaido, they form well-developed pure forests by themselves. They grow rapidly and attain 60 feet in twenty-five years, and are found most profitable and the best wood for making safety matches.

The visitor to Japan is at once impressed with the green, tree-covered hills and mountain slopes that are clothed almost to the sea. Those forests are of untold value, for they are not only important in the basic economy of the country, but they prevent erosion and land-slides, which, but for the trees, would ruin many fruitful valleys. They hold back the heavy rainfall, and release it gradually as needed for flooding the paddy fields in the lower valleys. World War II has greatly depleted these forests, and the fertility of much of the agricultural land is now being threatened, as the protective forest covering has been removed to manufacture charcoal for war industries and rayon for clothing the people. Her forests will be still further taxed for the re-building of two million homes destroyed by fire or bombs during the war, for most Japanese houses are made of wood and paper and other forest products. With meagre supplies of coal, the forests provide fuel both for heating and cooking and for industrial use, and rayon made from spruce and other trees is increasingly used in clothing the people—for Japan must provide her requirements with little or no help from the outside world. Japan is fortunate in having forest resources adequate to meet her urgent needs.

The economic aspect of her forests is, however, not the most important to the people of Japan, for they look to the trees for their inspiration in daily life. They are real tree-lovers and from time immemorial have shown a sympathetic understanding of the forests that protect the mountainsides and make it possible for the dense population to survive in the crowded islands. It would be interesting to discover the origin of this deep regard, which exists, not only for individual trees, but for the whole green mantle upon which very existence depends. Were the Japanese descendants of the people of Mu, which suffered so great a catastrophe? Was it there, in that ancient continent, that they learnt their lesson of soil conservation?

Of all the Japanese trees, sugi, *Cryptomeria japonica*, is the most greatly revered. This beautiful conifer, which looks so much like the big tree of the high Sierras of California, has been planted in extensive forests for hundreds of years. The world's grandest tree memorial is the forty-mile long avenue of sugi at Nikko. It was planted about 300 years ago by a Dalmyo who was too poor to offer a more costly tribute to the shrines at Nikko. Many of the individual trees are over 5 feet in diameter, and in places their trunks are so close together that they look like a wall of columns. This remarkable avenue constantly curves and bends, for, according to ancient beliefs, any evil spirits intent on pursuing the people would be thus thwarted and hindered.

Among the Japanese, trees are regarded as living entities which possess spirits, and before felling is begun the spirit of the tree has to be placated by a simple ceremony, in which the tree's permission is asked before felling. It is significant that the Maoris, who might also have been survivors of the Continent of Mu, use a similar ceremony before they fell a forest tree. They, too, are wood craftsmen of a high order. In Nippon, as in no other country in the world, may be found the combination of that reverent love for tree and forest with such a deep artistic appreciation and craftsmanship which uses the wood of the trees to its greatest advantage. The Japanese look to their forests, not in vain, for shelter and fuel, as well as for almost every kind of domestic requirement, and they depend upon what the forest yields, harvesting it as a precious crop to meet their needs; but never do they abuse their woodlands by reckless felling, and they always have regard to their regeneration. They plant and tend their trees for the future, just as they harvest and sow other crops. Before the Japanese people were prostituted by industrialism, no people used wood so thoughtfully or for so many domestic purposes. Their lacquered wood bowls are beautifully turned and withstand long use, even for hot food and drinks. No people employ the use of wood more effectively or treasure it more highly than their craftsmen, who value the natural grain with which they ornament their houses and temples. This reverence and sympathy, not only for the living trees, but for the wood of the forest, has sprung from their religious belief in the oneness of all living things. The Grand Temples at Ise, simple in design and form, built from flawless hinoki, have come down through the centuries as evidence of a profound religious belief. No craftsman may fell or prepare the temple trees unless he is "pure in heart". Western civilization, with its rush for gain and craze for mass production, may well take a lesson from the Orient, where man can still live close to Nature and where reverence is paid to the natural resources of the earth.

Chapter Sixteen

THE MAGIC ISLANDS

By the waters of Babylon we sat down and wept.

Psalm 137: 1.

TO THE TRAVELLER THE ISLANDS OF THE PACIFIC ARE steeped in romance, and they never fail to cast a mysterious spell over the mind of the voyager, whether he or she visits them by air or sea or is introduced to their charms by a travelogue film or the pages of a treasured book. The very mention of their names is as music: Hawaii, Tahiti, Rarotonga, Bali, Java—these are as notes in an entrancing symphony. Many travel-stories have been written about them, and many are the romantic pages which have depicted the life idyllic among the aborigines who bask on sandy beaches under the shade of palms, laze in their canoes, or dive in clear waters filled with bright-hued coral and little fish of many colours. Many are the coral reefs, decked with a patchwork of angelic green, bordered by waterways of deepest blue. Here are entrancing lagoons studded with little islands, where coconut palms wave their fronds and bananas and pineapples grow with superb luxuriance unequalled elsewhere.

At one time, maybe, these magic islands were part of a mighty continent which may have been the motherland of the world. Recent research has brought to light a growing volume of evidence to show that this continent did exist. Its tragic disappearance has not yet been fully explained, but it either subsided or was eroded away, leaving but mountain peaks visible above the water. Coral reefs have formed around many of these fascinating islands which we would visit.

Setting out from the east coast of Africa, the spice island of Zanzibar is the first port of call. This is the home of nutmeg and cashew, tiny by comparison with Madagascar, the fifth largest island in the world, which is about four times as large as England and Wales, for it is close on 1,000 miles long and over 350 miles in its greatest breadth. In days gone by, when man was yet young, the forests were religiously guarded. It was the sacred duty of the king, who was also high priest, to protect the trees and forests, particularly where they formed catchment areas at the sources of springs and rivers. Primitive man soon came to recognize the close association between trees and water and his dependence upon both for his existence. That might well account for the protection of the forests from the earliest times in Madagascar.

It is interesting to note that there are no family names in this island, and almost every personal name is drawn from the language of everyday life and signifies some common action or object, such as a tree, a plant, or a bird. This is evidence that the people, or the ancient rulers, were aware of the kinship of man with every living thing. This custom had its drawbacks, for, such was the reverence paid by the island dwellers to their kingly priests, whenever one of these words was taken as the name of their chief it became sacred and could no longer be used for the object it denoted: hence a new name had to be invented. It is little wonder that the visitor meets with language difficulties!

The dried-up beds of ancient lakes would indicate that in times gone by the hills were better clothed with forests than they are to-day. Even now the lake regions are fertile and well wooded, especially in the eastern side of the island, though a large district in the south-west is barren. Erosion and soil deterioration might have been worse but for the fact that all round this mountainous island is an almost unbroken belt of forest, from ten to forty miles across, containing many trees treasured for their timber and forest interest. Here we find the traveller's tree, *Ravenala madagascariensis*, the raffia palm, the lace-leaf, the beef-wood tree, *Casuarina equisetifolia*, several species of small pandana, and bamboo. Three-fourths of the species and one-sixth of the genera of the plants are endemic or native only to Madagascar, showing that the island is of great antiquity. About 4,100 indigenous species are now known, and there is a single family with twenty-four species confined to the island. There is scope for large-scale afforestation, particularly on the east and north-east, and the Malagasy are likely to follow any lead given, for they have an inherent regard for their trees and forests, around which many a folk-tale has been woven.

There is magic in the very remoteness of the 100 tiny islands of the Seychelles, where grows the largest fruit in the world. It is one of the palm coconut trees, *Lodoicea seychellarum*. Its gigantic fruits take six years to develop. Inside the shell are found two or three nuts, and it is popularly known as the sea coconut or coco-de-mer.

Ceylon has a land area of 25,500 square miles, and a total forest area of over 16,000 square miles, three-quarters of this being unprofitable or inaccessible. Tea plantations cover much of the land, which was at one time primeval forest. Coffee, which itself is a forest tree, was the first popular plantation crop in the early days of British colonization. Sir Samuel Baker's farm in Nuwara Eliya was among the best known, but disease resulting from the wholesale clearing of the forests and the introduction of monoculture cost Ceylon £15,000,000, destroyed the popularity of coffee as a crop, and tea took its place. Forest growth is strong, and many ancient buildings and temples have been swallowed by the jungle, which has reclaimed land where people once lived in their crowded cities.

To a visitor it would seem that this enchanting island was "draped with forests of perennial green", for the hills tower magnificently until they are lost in clouds and mists. Undulating plains cover four-fifths of the island, while one-fifth is occupied by the mountain of the Central South which rises to 8,000 feet above sea-level. Most of the trees of Ceylon are found nowhere else in the world, though some of them, and many of the plants, are closely allied to those of the Malay islands and peninsula. The trees are evergreen and form thick jungles with gregarious plants known as nilu, a species of *Strobilanthlae*, which flower at regular intervals of five, six, or seven years. In the mountain forests, tree ferns luxuriate to a height of 25 feet. Scarlet-flowering rhododendrons add to the beauty of the natural bush.

In the low-lying country coconut palms are much in evidence, and a beautiful areca palm, the feathery jaggery, or kitual, and the lordly talipat are among the species which enhance the glories of the vegetation. Calamander, satinwood, and ebony are among the timber trees of special value. In the dry forest region in the north of Ceylon may be found the palmita or Trincomali wood and ebony. The characteristic palm of these regions and the Peninsula of Jaffna is the palmyra, *Borassus flabelliformis*. The coconut, cinnamon, and several species of pepper are native to the island.

It is to be regretted that extensive cutting of the forests has denuded the mountainsides, the trees having been felled for the purpose of making plantations. The improvident practice of native shifting cultivation known as *chena* has also been responsible for denuding much of the island. When I visited Ceylon, I had the privilege of broadcasting in three languages, and urged the hill cultivators to plant trees on their old farms before forsaking them to make fresh ones; and of recent years the Forestry Department has met with some success in persuading the people to establish in this way potential forests for the future.

Before leaving this enchanting island, I must mention that high among the mountains near the ancient capital, Kandy, are the famous Peredinia Gardens. These gardens, which are the Kew of the East, contain one of the finest collections of tropical trees in the world. For many years the curator has published a book describing the plants and trees of his arboretum with concise notes for their cultivation. As a forest officer in Equatorial Africa, I found this book invaluable whenever laying out a new station. Years afterwards I had the pleasure of spending some days in the gardens near Kandy, and was able to see the numerous species of trees growing side by side, and to study their various characteristics at close range. I am so indebted to the curators of this beautiful arboretum that I feel bound to pay this tribute for the great contribution they have made to planting, not only in Ceylon, but throughout the tropical and sub-tropical regions of the earth. There is great scope in Ceylon for an active branch of the Men of the Trees to carry on an educational campaign, both among planters and indigenous peoples.

There are two groups of islands in the Bay of Bengal, the Andamans and the Nicobars, which together formed a province of British India. They contain dense tropical forests, and the climate is warm and moist with heavy rainfall. There are many islands off the Malay Peninsula, which itself contains 41,390 square miles of forest, or 78·8 per cent of the total land area. About 40,770 square miles of this consists of hardwood trees, and only 620 square miles of conifers. Before World War II Malay produced half the world's supply of rubber.

Sumatra is the largest of the great Cunda islands and is nearly as large as Spain, for, with the many islands along its coasts, it is probably 180,000 square miles in extent. The Equator runs through the middle of it and the greatest length is 1,115 miles. This great island has its own mountain system, with several ranges towering to 1,200 feet above sea level with intervening plateaux and valleys. Geologically speaking the kernel of Sumatra consists of slates and clay schists of high antiquity, with granite sometimes visible; but the whole has been modified by strata of the carboniferous formations, and in later periods by Tertiary breccias, sandstones, marls, and coral beds. Volcanoes have played an important part in embossing the surface and, only sixty-four years ago, the southern end of Sumatra was involved in the great Krakatao eruption. The lovely mountain lakes are largely volcanic. Many of these have been formed by the craters falling in on themselves in the manner of Crater Lake in the north-west Pacific coast of America. The rivers are fed by an abundant rainfall, which may be over 80 inches a year, and the humid climate and volcanic soil produce ideal conditions for tree growth.

There are at least 400 varieties of timber trees native to the island, and vast areas of the mountain regions are covered by virgin forests as yet not fully explored by botanists and foresters. The total forest area has been estimated at 113,000 square miles, or about six times that of the forest area of Spain, for nearly sixty-three per cent of the total land area is forest. The climate and soil make Sumatra particularly suitable for agriculture and plantations. Rice is a staple crop, and sugar is grown from canes and arage palm, while coffee and coconuts, as well as pepper, sago, maize, sweet potatoes, and yams, have long been cultivated. As recently as the beginning of the twentieth century, extensive rubber plantations have been made and nearly half a million acres planted.

The forests of Java and Madura are 10,000 square miles in

extent and comprise nearly twenty per cent of the land area, which is 51,000 square miles. These mountainous islands have forty-three volcanoes, several of which are still active. There are four distinct botanical zones, the lowest of them being characterized by tropical forests, with palms and mangroves which flourish between high and low tides and in tidal creeks. The second region is that of the plantations, where tea, coffee, cinchona, sugar, and maize are grown. Grasses, herbs, and shrubs are characteristic of the third zone, and the fourth is alpine. Many are the varieties of trees to be found, as might well be expected in a country with such a great variety of climate and aspect. Oaks have been known to thrive above an altitude of 4,500 feet, while in Sumatra they come down to 500 or even 100 feet above sea level.

In the short space of a century the population of Java has sprung from about 9 to 50 millions. An ever increasing demand will inevitably be made upon the forests, and permanent protection-forests will be needed to regulate water flow.

There is a strange custom sometimes practised when rain is wanted. Two men will select supple rods and flog each other until the blood flows down their backs in imitation of rain. Fraser suggests that the prophets of Baal, who sought to procure rain by cutting themselves with knives till the blood gushed out, may have acted on the same principle. A simpler and more humane way of assuring precipitation is to plant trees.

Next to Greenland and New Guinea, Borneo is the largest island in the world. To reach it from the south, the Java Sea is crossed. The length of the island is about 800 miles and its breadth 700; it contains a total area of 284,000 square miles. The north-eastern part is occupied by the states of Sarawak, Brunei, and North Borneo; its total land area is 84,000 square miles with a total forest area of 73·7 per cent. The country is mountainous, the highest points range from 4,000 feet to 8,000 feet; broadly speaking, the whole country is corrugated and gnarled in a most irregular manner. This is the result of the process of denudation carried on by the tropical rains, which, through the ages, have scooped out interior valleys and plains and laid down vast level tracks that extend eastwards into the morass-like delves.

Gum trees near Wilpina.

Aborigine climbing a Eucalyptus Tree, North Queensland.

Major Patrick M. Synge, who was a member of the Oxford Expedition to Sarawak, in his book, *Borneo Jungle*, describes the forests as "so luxuriant that they seemed a frenzy of greens, a solid wall, a never-ending skyscraper of leaves overhanging the water's edge, behind darkness and mystery". Borneo is indeed a superb forest country. The giants of the tropical forest are often festooned with woody lianas, and many choice orchids or pitcher plants may be found by the explorer. The people follow the practice of shifting cultivation. They hack their way into the jungle, and clear areas in which they grow their food crops. After they have reaped them, they move on to repeat the same destructive process. When the paddy-field is left deserted, the ground soon becomes reclothed with tropic vegetation. Whereas it is possible to walk through the virgin forest, it is necessary to hack a way through the dense jungle that takes possession of such clearings.

The forests produce many and valuable trees, including iron wood, bilian, teak, ebony, sandal-wood, die woods, and the camphor of Brunei which is the best in Asia. The mohur tree, which is a popular timber, reaches a height of 80 feet, and the kaladang, which is much sought after for shipmasts, reaches a height of 200 feet. Nutmegs, cloves, cinnamon, pepper, ginger, and sugar cane are among the many crops that are cultivated. When we think of those deep tropical forests, we are apt to conjure up a mental picture of a paradise of many blossoms which vie with each other in the brightness of their colouring, whereas, in fact, one has to hunt for the flowers of the trees. Even if one is fortunate enough to find a fallen blossom on a forest trail, the canopy of the forest denizens is so closely interwoven that it is quite a feat to determine the tree from which it came. Many tree flowers are ridiculously small in comparison with the flowers of other plants, and some are quite inconspicuous.

The glory of the tropical forest is the shimmery green of luxuriant foliage, contrasting with greens of more sombre hue. But there are times when the explorer becomes satiated with beauty. There is monotony in the evergreen rain forest, for there is none of the freshness of foliage that springs to clothe naked branches in colder climes, nor is there any temperate

L

autumn to transform the leaves into bright colourings.
Throughout the year there is little variety, for there is no pause
in the growing period, the high temperature and high humidity
encouraging unceasing growth; it is perpetual summer. The
rings by which a tree records its age in temperate countries are
unknown. The work of colonization goes on in the tree-tops,
and here, unobserved by man, seed-production is carried on by
brightly-coloured butterflies and many tiny insects which assist
the trees to perpetuate their species. Life in the tree tops is
dazzlingly beautiful; the dance of life goes on in timeless space.
There is a ruthless rhythm in the intensity of growth, where
everything germinates and begins to thrust its way upwards in
bloodless conflict for a place in the sun. The earth itself is a
child of the sun, and its tree children are ever striving to get
nearer their distant father. In Borneo and other volcanic islands
of the Pacific we are reminded of this, for the thermal energy
is nearer the surface. This generates electro-magnetic currents
which stimulate growth.

Borneo is a plant-collector's paradise, and provides a largely
unexplored field for botanists. There is a lure in the green
glory of its forest fastness which will call the traveller back and
back to further exploration.

The Philippine Islands, named after Philip II of Spain, form
a northern section of the Malay Archipelago, separated from
the rest by the Sulu and Celebes Seas. Of the total land area of
115,000 square miles, the forest area is 40,000 square miles;
38,000 square miles are hardwoods and 2,000 square miles
conifers. The islands were discovered in 1521 by Magellan,
during his great voyage round the globe. Legaspi, who came
from Mexico in 1565, established a Spanish colony in the
islands. In the succeeding centuries, the colonists had to defend
themselves against the Portuguese, Chinese, Dutch, English,
and Moors. After the destruction of the Spanish Fleet by
Admiral Dewey at the time of the Spanish-American War in
1898, the Philippines were ceded to the U.S.A. Under
American rule the islands experienced administrative and
economic advancement, and the achievement of American
foresters does credit to the American Forestry Service. The
names of Aheren, Pinchot, Bryant, and others are well known.

During visits to America I had the privilege of meeting both Major Aheren and Gifford Pinchot. The latter was the first forester of the U.S.A. to be appointed by Theodore Roosevelt at the time of the inauguration of the forestry service. He is better known to-day as the Governor of Pennsylvania, but his early contribution to the science of forestry will always be remembered. These men were great pioneers in the field of forestry, both in the Philippines and in their native land. It was their vision and courage, backed by scientific knowledge, that provided for the mapping out of the forest areas of the Philippines, island by island, when the lands were classified and working plans drawn up between 1905 and 1913. Among other pioneer foresters were Merril, Whitford, Foxworthy, Matthews, Merrit, Cuzan, Shfersesne, Nash, and, last but not least, Corran, to whom I am indebted for bringing these names to my mind. Those young men came fresh to their new colony from the remnants of American timber-lands. They had seen the spoliation by lumbermen in their own country and were determined that the forests of their new colonies should be put on a sound footing and be saved for all time for the people of the Philippines. Under the wise administration of Arthur Fischer, now Colonel Fischer, the last American chief of the Philippine Forest Service, these forests, which are among the finest in the world, were placed on a sustained yield basis under scientific management. Before the fateful incident of Pearl Harbour, the Philippines possessed an efficient staff of Philippino foresters who were trained for the most part at the School of Forestry at Los Banos. It is earnestly hoped that many of these young men have survived the war, for in their hands will rest the future of the forests in the Philippines. The war made great demands upon those forests for all kinds of construction materials and fuel wood for sugar mills, as well as alcohol for the Japanese transports. Many of the young trees planted by the students of the forestry school were cut by the Japanese for bridge-building and for wooden ships. The school plantation included teak and Honduras mahogany over 100 feet high. Many of these trees were sacrificed during hostilities, but, fortunately, the bulk of the forest wealth of the Philippines remains and is now helping to heal the scars of war. It is to be hoped that the future of one of the most wonderful hardwood forests of the world will be safe in the hands of hundreds of trained Philippino forest officers, who will see to it that the wealth of their woods is economically harvested and regenerated for perpetual use.

The same warm currents that touch the eastern coasts of the Philippines sweep northwards to the shores of Formosa, where there are splendid primeval forests covering the greater part of the island. Of the 13,900 square miles of land area, 11,000 square miles is forest.

Far out in the Pacific are the Ladrones or Mariana Islands, a group of fifteen discovered by Magellan. The five which are to the south are low and flat; those to the north mountainous. Most are thickly wooded, and all are well watered and fruitful. Timber is exported from Guam.

The Caroline Islands, another group in the western Pacific, are all fertile and well watered, and many of the low-lying lagoons are well wooded.

A contrast to these tiny islands is Celebes, the third largest and the central island of the Malay Archipelago. With its adjoining islands it is variously estimated to contain an area of from 72,000 to 78,000 square miles and has about 19,000 square miles of forest, which approximates to twenty-six per cent of the total land area. To the north the Sea of Celebes separates this great island from Borneo. It is a Dutch possession with numerous small native states. The east end of the eastern peninsula is subject to earthquakes and contains eleven volcanoes, some of which are active; for instance, Mount Sapoetan, 5,938 feet, and Mount Klabat, which reaches a height of 6,559 feet. There are numerous hot springs and sulphur lakes in this mountainous volcanic area. The highest mountains are Latimojong, which is 11,470 feet, and Lombo Batang, 10,000 feet. The uplands of the southern peninsula have the best forests. The crops include rice, maize, coffee, sugar, tobacco, indigo, areca, betel, pepper, clove, and nutmeg, which last grows wild. The Macassar oil tree, ebony and sandalwood, oak, teak, and cedar are among the better-known trees. The Minahassa district is famous for producing coffee of a remarkably fine flavour.

The Bugis and Mangkassars of the South Peninsula, tall, with fine figures and comparatively fair in complexion, are the dominant native race and are good sailors.

Away to the south is Timor, with a range of wood-clad mountains that run throughout the island chain, stretching eastwards from Java, with a total area of about 12,000 square miles; but its comparatively dry climate produces less luxuriant vegetation than that of Java.

The greatest island of Australasia is New Guinea, formerly known as Papua. This great tropical forest land is separated from the continent of Australia by the shallow, island-studded Torres Strait, only eighty or ninety miles wide at the narrowest part. There is no doubt that the two regions at one time formed continuous land, and it has been suggested that an upheaval of less than 60 fathoms would again unite them.

New Guinea appears to have been first sighted by D'Abreu in 1511, and first visited by de Meneses about 1526 and by Alvaro de Saavedra in 1528. It was named from the resemblance of its inhabitants to those of the Guinea coast in West Africa. In 1914 it was occupied by an Australian force, and the Commonwealth of Australia holds it by mandate. It is essentially a mountainous country with lofty ranges, its highest mountain being 13,000 feet. There are elevated plateaux which are used as health resorts by the officials and traders from the coast. The whole of New Guinea lies in the track of the south-east trade winds, prevailing from March to October and charged with much moisture from the Pacific. These are followed for the rest of the year by the north-west monsoons, whose rain-bearing clouds are condensed on the cooler Alpine slopes of the island, so that the rain- or snow-fall is considerable in every part of the country. This, combined with an average high temperature of from 80° to 90°, results in a hot, moist climate on all the low-lying coastlands and river valleys, making them suitable for large-scale afforestation.

Great is the variety of trees found after passing through the domains of tropical plants. Such temperate or sub-tropical growths as the cedar, oak, fig, acacia, pine, and tree fern are found on the higher slopes, and with them may be seen wild strawberries, forget-me-nots, daisies, buttercups, and other plants familiar in Britain. Towards the summits, these are succeeded by true Alpine flora, in which Himalayan, Bornean, New Zealand, and sub-Antarctic forms are numerously represented. In general, tree vegetation ceases at about 11,000 feet and shrub at 12,000, the latter being overlapped by the alpine zone. In New Guinea it is found that the Asiatic Malayan floras are far more richly represented than the Australian, as is demonstrated by the rare occurrence of the eucalyptus. Indigenous forms are numerous and include many species of palm. Of the total land area of British New Guinea, which is 170,000 square miles, as much as 136,000 square miles is forest, or over eighty per cent. It is sparsely populated, for there are 97 acres per head of population, whereas, for instance, in Japan, there is considerably less than 1 acre per man.

East of New Guinea are the Solomon Islands, which stretch south-east in two parallel chains for 600 miles towards the Santa Cruz group. They have a total estimated area of 17,000 square miles, 10,000 square miles of which is forest. There is an extraordinarily heavy annual rainfall, estimated at 400 or even 500 inches on the mountains and 150 on the coasts.

New Britain, an island of the Bismarck Archipelago, separated from the north-eastern coast of New Guinea by the Dampier Strait, is well wooded in the interior. With the other islands of this Archipelago, the total land area is 20,000 square miles, half of it forest. The native folk are famous for their handsome canoes, with sails and outriggers. The interior is little known to botanists, and there is great scope for the plant-hunter.

New Caledonia, belonging to France, lies midway between the Fiji Islands and the east coast of Queensland. The Loyalty Islands, Isle of Pines, and some others, with a total area of 1,250 square miles, are politically dependent upon New Caledonia, which is 6,450 square miles. Below its mountain summits the forest covering is generally unbroken and contains many useful timber trees.

The New Hebrides group consists of thirty islands, most of which have the appearance of being well wooded, but, with a total area of 5,700 square miles, 700 only are classed as forest.

The Fiji Islands were sighted in 1643 by Tasman, the great Dutch sailor after whom Tasmania has been named. But, like many of the South Sea islands, the Fiji Archipelago was little known before the nineteenth century. The islands are from 200 to 250 in number, and lie in a ring open on the southern side in a manner resembling the West Indies. The total area of the colony is given as 7,083 square miles, or about the same size as Wales.

The Fiji Islands are of volcanic formation, surrounded by coral reefs which form natural breakwaters and good harbours. The rainfall is abundant in the warm season, and the land is most heavily timbered on the south-eastern, the windward side of the islands. On the leeward side the country is largely open grassland. The islands have considerable agricultural resources.

All these islands and many hundreds of others, some of which are entirely of coral formation, such as the Marshall islands, east of the Carolines, and the Gilbert islands, are to be found in this largest of oceans which occupies one-half of the water surface of the globe and more than one-third of the whole area of the world. A visitor to this planet would get the impression that a great continent was missing and that these islands are but the mountain tops of a submerged land. Indeed, the proofs of the former existence of this great continent in the Pacific are now being presented. The record of the destruction of Mu, the capital motherland of man, is a terrifying story, but it is slowly coming to light through recent translations of stone and brick tablets. They relate how the Naacals had originally come from the motherland in the centre of the Pacific, of the creation of man, and his advent in this land. Records in Maya, Egypt, and India describe this land of Mu and its destruction when the earth's crust was broken up and the waters of the Pacific rolled over her, leaving only water where once there was a mighty civilization.

Apart from these records on stone, burnt clay, or on the cliffs, are the existing ruins, which by their location and their symbols tell of the West Continent of the motherland of Mu. On some of the South Sea Islands, notably Easter, Mangaia, Tonga-tabu Panapi, and the Ladrones or Marianas Islands,

there stand to-day vestiges of old stone temples which go back
to the time of Mu. It has been estimated that the southern
boundary of the lost land mass was somewhere between Easter
Island and the Fijis. It appears to have been over 5,000 miles
from east to west, and over 3,000 miles from north to south. Mu
was a beautiful, tropical country, with vast plains and valleys
covered with rich grazing grasses and tilled fields, while the
low, rolling hills were clothed with luxuriant vegetation.
Herds of "mighty mastodons and elephants" roamed through
the land, and the whole teemed with gay and happy life. The
recorded population of about 60 million was highly civilized
in the modern sense of the word, and there was "no savagery
on the face of the earth nor had there ever been", since all the
peoples on the earth were children of Mu, the one motherland.
The dominant race were "great navigators who took their ships
over the world from the eastern to western oceans and from
the northern to the southern seas; . . . they were also learned
architects who built great temples and palaces of stone". They
carved and set up mighty monoliths as monuments. The
people of Mu were colonists and had established themselves in
all parts of the earth. In their great empire, art, industry,
learning, and trade reached its zenith. Then a fearful visitation
overtook them and their end came.

The authoritative accounts differ as to how long the period
of destruction continued before the final subsidence of the continent occurred. Ancient writings graphically relate how
during the night Mu was torn asunder and rent to pieces and
with thunderous roarings the doomed land sank and was
covered with water, only mountains and points of land here
and there remaining to mark the site. One can hardly imagine
the plight of the survivors. Such ridges and points as were not
submerged may well have been crowded with people from the
sinking land. Huddled together with little food and threatened
by exposure, few remained after the dreadful ordeal. Those
that did survive must have been crowded together on mere
specks of land, thousands of miles from any mainland, without
boats, ships, or food. In such circumstances, many may have
become hopelessly insane, driven mad by sheer horror. To
exist, one thing alone was left to them: "to go down into the

Canadian spruce for aeroplane construction.

On the next two pages: Fighting a forest fire near the Santa Lucia National Park, U.S.A.

American contrasts: log jam on Montreal river, and—

—sand dunes at Salado Wash.

lowest depths of savagery", and for a time at least live upon one another. Leaves of palms and foliage must in future be their dress; stones, spears, and arrows must be their weapons, and their cutting tools fashioned from stones and shells. Their first need was food. Many had died from hunger and exposure, and as these died their bodies became the food of survivors. In this manner came the first cannibalism, and thus the survivors of the highest civilization sank to the lowest savagery, which has continued through the ages.

By remains of ancient temples found on the South Sea Islands, supported by records and traditions, it is shown that the Pacific Islanders, in spite of their present savage and semi-savage state, were not always so. It is clearly established that they are descendants of highly civilized peoples. No ancient record has ever been found to show that such ways of life existed on any spot of the earth's surface prior to the destruction of Mu.

The ancient dwellers had reached a state of ultra-urbanization, and had been repeatedly warned by their rulers and priests that destruction would come upon them. The Lhasa record discovered by Schliemann in the old Buddhist temple of Lhasa in Tibet gives this account:

"When the star of Bal fell on the place where now is only the sky and the sea, the seven cities with their golden gates and transparent temples quivered and shook like the leaves in a storm, and, behold, a flood of fire and smoke arose from the palaces. Agonies and cries of the multitude filled the air. They sought refuge in their temples and citadels, and the wise Mu—the Hieratic Ra Mu—arose and said to them: 'Did I not predict all this?' And the womenkind and the men in their precious stones and shining garments lamented 'Mu, save us!' and Mu replied, 'You shall all die together with your servants and your riches, and from your ashes new nations shall arise. If they forget they are superior *not because of what they put on but what they put out* the same will befall them.' Flames and smoke choked the words of Mu: the land and its inhabitants were torn to pieces and swallowed up by the depths."

Bal is a Maya word meaning "Lord of the Fields". The opinion has been expressed that "transparent temples" is a mistranslation. These temples were not built of glass or any other transparent substance, but were open or roofless temples so constructed that the rays of Ra, the sun, could fall upon the heads of those who were in prayer and supplication within the temple, for they were open to the sky, like the Parsee temples of to-day.

The very latest theory in relation to world floods might suggest that Mu was gradually engulfed, the land having been eroded away after its forest covering had been removed for non-conservative agriculture. Only the mountains, which were covered with forest, remained to become the magic isles of the Pacific.

In the Hawaiian music of to-day may be sensed the ever-recurring note of tragedy and pathos, and in the friendly bearing of the islanders there is many a touch of nobility which bespeaks a long past of greatness.

Chapter Seventeen

KAURIS AND MAORIS

One crash, the death-hymn of the perfect tree,
Declares the close of its green century.
Low lies the plant to whose creation went
Sweet influence from every element;
Whose living towers the years conspired to build,
Whose giddy top the morning loved to gild.

Emerson.

WITH THEIR PRIMITIVE GRANDEUR, THE KAURI TREES OF New Zealand form a living link with past ages, and in their delectable home, cut off from the rest of the world, their forests have not been invaded by mammals or other forms of aggressive life until recent times.

For millennia, surrounded by his lesser tree brethren, the giant kauri has reigned in the green glory of his forest domain. He and his sires of bygone ages experienced land upheavals and submersions and yet remained to re-establish their evergreen kingdom on the new land as it rose out of the sea. From his forest sanctuary he looked on snow-clad mountain peaks while he felt the warmth of subterranean springs and his growth was nourished by volcanic ash from the underworld. This king of forest trees has survived all cosmic changes, and to-day, in his arboreal majesty, shares honours with the Californian sequoias, a veritable patriarch among trees.

The kauri pine, *Agathis australis*, is not only the most outstanding tree of New Zealand but in the quality of its economic products and scientific interest it rivals all other living trees. The realm of the kauri pine is between latitudes 35° and 37° south, which corresponds to Melbourne and Valparaiso. It is farther south than the Cape of Good Hope, though I believe it would thrive in Cape Colony. In the Northern Hemisphere, it would be on the same latitude as Tokyo, Wei-hai-wei, Chitral, Tehran, Gibraltar, the Grand Canyon and Monterey. With the

co-operation of the countries in their zones it would be interesting to plant groups or belts of kauris, with their natural
nurse trees, around the world. Its seed is contained in a cone, 1½
to 2 inches in diameter, made up of a number of flat brown
scales, each covering a single scale-like seed. It grows naturally
in mixed forests of shade-bearing species where there is a
luxuriant growth of other lesser plants; these they overtop
when they reach their full height.

The largest kauri is reputed to have been 93 feet in girth, but
the greatest tree reported with certainty was 66 feet in cir-
cumference and 100 feet to the first branch. This massive tree
contained 30,000 cubic feet of wood. The timber of such a tree
would weigh about 500 tons and would contain enough planks
of 1 inch thick to cover an area of nearly 5 acres. The largest
kauri now standing is approximately 51 feet in girth, with an
estimated volume of about 17,000 cubic feet.

Besides timber, they yield a valuable gum. I once saw a
Maori climbing one of the bigger trees to collect gum from
the forked branches, and he seemed to be walking up it
with as much ease as a fly walks up the wall of a room. He had
iron points in the toes of his boots and was armed with two
hammer-shaped axes, rather like a mountaineer's ice-pick, one
of which he carried in each hand. These he drove alternately
into the trunk of the tree to help himself up, using the sharp
points in the toes of his boots as climbing irons. He carried a
rope with which he let himself down as soon as he had collected the gum. This precious gum, much sought after for
varnishes, is sometimes found beside the root of these trees,
where it has been buried under the surface for many years. It is
also dug up from the ground or dredged from swamps, where
forests of these trees have formerly grown, and even lies mingled
in the cold stratum of the Tertiary deposit. The new gum is
whitish in colour but in time it turns a dull amber. Often tiny
flies and insects are seen embalmed in the middle of a lump.
The finest quality is used for amber beads. During the past
century, over twenty-two million pounds' worth of this so-called
minor forest product has been exported from the kauri forest
region.

A remarkable feature of the kauri is its trunk, which has

hardly any taper, but grows a cylindrical bole over 100 feet high, surmounted by an umbrella-shaped crown of olive green foliage. Unlike the redwoods and many conifers of the Northern Hemisphere, which have conical forms and drooping branches to provide protection against snow break, this tree does not need much protection, for the aspect of its forests is tropical.

I shall never forget my first sight of these lordly trees in the Waipoua Forest. They stood in the virgin bush, which had been opened up by a clearing, so that their mighty buttresses appeared to form a colonnade. Overawed by their kingly dignity, I felt that I might have been standing in an ancient Greek Temple, for their huge trunks stood out in clear-cut relief backed by the sombre green of lesser forest growth.

Although the lower part of the trunks were usually branchless, they did not give the appearance of being bare, for these patriarch trees acted as host to a number of climbing ferns, lichens, and hanging grasses, while air plants and orchids draped their massive columns. Tough, woody lianas hung suspended in the air, and bushes, trees, and shrubs of every kind formed a tangled mass to cover the ground around their buttresses.

There was an incessant struggle for life, silent and serene. As I entered the forest parthenon, rays of light shot through the foliage and sunbeams danced on the fronds of climbing ferns and pendant grasses, and dappled the grey-brown trunks of those ancient friendly trees. They seemed to be beckoning me on into the inner recesses of a quiet world where time is not. I found myself standing close to the oldest tree of all. As I touched the gnarled old bark, I tried to visualize the happenings of the past. He had looked out on the glorious sunset of a former day. His forebears may have been planted by the giants of a past age. It may have been that his island home was once part of that great continent of Mu, but had escaped destruction through the protective covering provided by his forest. Eleven generations of his family had germinated, grown, and fought their way up through the tangled growth, looked out over the tree tops where they reigned for 1,000 years, and then returned to earth to complete the cycle before being reincarnated in their grandsons. For 110 centuries the silence of the forest was unbroken but for the note of the bell bird and his many feathered friends. Flightless birds there were in plenty, including the giant moa, which stood over 12 feet high, with legs the strength and size of those of a horse. He could not fly, but he had no enemies from whom he needed to escape; until one day, about 600 years ago, canoes were sighted and men who hunted them arrived on the scene. The silence of 100 centuries was broken, and for the first time the sound of the axe was heard. Kikaumako trees were being cut to make wood for men's fire-sticks. Other men were collecting dead sticks to cook their food. These men were the Maoris, who had come in their double canoes, sailing the ocean for 1,600 miles until they looked out on what they called the Land of Ao-Tea Roa, or the Land of the Shining Coast. They brought with them their wives and children and dogs, as well as rats which they had used for food on their long voyage. They found a flax plant, *Phormium tenax*, growing on the fringe of the forest, which they cut and from which they prepared fibres for making their garments. At first they obtained all their food from the sea and the forest, and made no farms, so the balance of Nature was not upset. The only clearings they made were for their *pas* or fortified villages. These they made with birches and tawa, and their canoes from the rimu, or red pine. They looked on the trees as their brothers, and would not unnecessarily harm them. Was not Tane, the Lord of Light, both father of the trees and of man? Their priests had taught them the ancient lore that trees were the first living things; they felt their kinship with the trees through their common father. When a Maori went to the forest to seek a tree for a new canoe, he would first ask its permission before felling it and then cover up the stump with foliage so as to protect the inlying spirit.

Life in the forest went on much the same as of yore, and the giant kauri looked out on the doings of these men with unconcern for another 300 years. The coming of Tasman, the Dutch sailor, in 1642 was a mere incident. As he looked upon the Shining Coast, it seemed to him that it had recently risen out of the sea, and he called it New-Sea-Land. He came, but he did not stay, and so the forest once more became tranquil. Nearly 150 years later the English arrived, and for the first

time the sound of steel axes was heard. Their brand of civilization made heavy demands on the forest, for they needed farms
in which to grow their food, and pastures for their flocks and
herds. Soon the conservative methods of the Maoris were dis-
credited and their simple ways of conservation were upset by
the newcomers. Maoriland, this ancient link with the land of
Mu, seemed ripe for exploitation. Its climate reminded these
colonists of England, and its forests provided a challenge to
their way of life. At the beginning of their settlement the kauri
forest was growing over a large part of the North Island from
Tauranga nearly to North Cape. It was felled without any
regard for its future, and, as in all pioneer stages of European
settlement, far more forest was destroyed to clear lands for
farming and grazing than was ever cut in to timber. But they
used it for every domestic purpose, and exported it to the
Australian colonies.

New Zealand proper has an area of 103,656 square miles;
though smaller in size, in configuration it is not unlike Japan.
It consists of two large islands called simply North and South,
and a number of small islands and islets, some of the latter
lying in tropical Polynesia, where the Cook group and Niue,
Penrhyn, and Suwarrow islands have been annexed to the
Dominion. New Zealand also governs most of the Samoan
Archipelago and, with Great Britain and Australia, shares the
administration of the phosphate-bearing island of Nauru. Her
Governor-General's sphere of influence extends to the Antarctic
territory of Rossland.

Of the great forest area that once clothed the hills and valleys,
only 20,700 square miles remain to-day, 10,600 square miles
of which consists of conifers and 10,100 square miles of hard
woods. Fortunately, more than half of the remaining total
forest area is classed by timber men as unprofitable or inaccessible. Nevertheless, those great areas serve their invaluable
function of moderating the climate and helping to distribute
and conserve the rain and melting snows. Twenty per cent of
the total land area is still forest, and there are over 8 acres per
head of population. The natural features of the land are full
of variety and interest; it is healthy and fertile and its scenery
is magnificent. There are long and lofty mountain ranges

with more than 150 peaks or cones exceeding 7,000 feet, and in
South Island sixteen rise to more than 10,000 feet. In the
south-west of that island much of the Southern Alps is in the
eternal snows, and their highest peak, 12,349 feet, is Ao-rangi,
the Mountain of the Sky, as the Maoris call it. Settlers called
this peak Mount Cook, after Captain Cook, who, in 1769,
landed at Waykanae beach close to the present site of Gisborne.
Mountains cover the greater part of South Island, running in
close parallel chains from south-west to north-east. As in
England, there is more rain on the west coast than on the east;
the rain-bringing winds from the south-west and north-west
are caught by the spinal ranges, so the country eastwards is
comparatively dry. For instance, the rainfall at Christchurch
is about the same as Norwich in East Anglia, 26 inches, while
that of Holitika is about 116 inches. In North Island the
mountain chains, though lower, show similar features.

All the forests of New Zealand come into the category of
rain forest, which may be divided into two distinct classes, sub-
tropical, or rain forest proper, and sub-Antarctic; the former
allied ecologically to tropical rain-forest, and the latter
dominated by species of *Nothofagus* as the only tall trees. Their
habitat extends through nine degrees of latitude, and they
occupy a vast area which is situated chiefly in the mountains
and hilly parts of both islands and on soil usually unsuited for
agriculture. With the exception of Totara the wood has not
been greatly used, though it is one of the most important of all
the indigenous trees. On the other hand, the sub-tropical rain
forest has been greatly reduced in area, because it is considered that the land on which this forest grows becomes at
once greatly enhanced in value when the tree covering is
replaced by meadow. The wood of these species has been much
in demand to make packing cases for the famous New Zealand
butter. The transformation from rain forest to sheep-pasture
and dairy land requires but one year for its accomplishment.
Through this remarkable fact the wealth of the Dominion in
large measure has been won—but at what a cost! Approximately 14 million acres of forest have been felled and sown to
grass in New Zealand. Not all of this has been successfully converted grassland, for at least 2 million acres have reverted to

The timber-line in the Rockies.

Where the glacier meets the timber-line.

secondary growth and scrub forest. It has been calculated that 4 million acres of standing forest awaits "development".

When it is considered that so large an area has already been deprived of its forest cover, it is remarkable that the country has so far been spared from serious erosion. It is true that a great deal of the soil wash was prevented by sowing the grass seeds on the "burn", and the climatic conditions were favourable to rapid germination, so that the grass was able to establish itself before there was any serious damage done by rain or wind. At any rate, the destruction of the virgin forests, from whatever cause, has been carried to a dangerous length. Many of the hills are now growing an inferior type of grass which does not provide adequate covering, and after a heavy downpour the murky streams are a danger signal which should be heeded.

It is the very isolation of New Zealand that makes it of interest to the student of forest ecology. In that country may be seen every transition from virgin tree communities to completely artificial ones. The land is rich in ecological experiments of various kinds, such as the burning of vegetation, different methods of agriculture, the presence or absence of certain exotic mammals, the fencing of a piece of ground, or the incoming of a new weed. Northern weeds are a serious pest. Gorse and broom introduced by the colonists are rampaging over millions of acres, weeping willows have choked many streams, and weeds, like other things, seem to grow more vigorously than in their native land.

The student has an opportunity of studying the various stages of draining swamps or witnessing a virgin forest turned into a sheep run. Even a neglected farm will provide valuable data and furnish splendid material for studies of great importance and intense scientific interest. It is possible in a day's ride to study the deterioration of land from virgin forest, through successive years of farming or grazing to examples of erosion and landslides.

Perhaps nothing is of greater interest in New Zealand's plant ecology than the effect of the multitudes of grazing and browsing mammals of many kinds upon a vegetation which had come into being unprepared for such an invasion. For

M

some time many of the forests were immune from their attacks, but now there is one great herd of deer from some distance north of south latitude 30° to south latitude 47·20°.

It is to be regretted that once the original forest cover has been removed it will not return naturally, and often less valuable species takes its place.

Rimu, or the red pine, *Dacrydium cupressinum*, is one of the most outstanding timber trees in New Zealand and covers about forty-five per cent of the forests. The three Podocarps, miro, *Podocarpus ferrugineus*, matai, *Podocarpus spicatus*, and totara, *Podocarpus totara*, contribute five per cent each. Two hardwood birches, tawa, *Beilschmiedia tawa*, and tawhai, or red beech, *Nothofagus fusca*, Southland or silver beech, *Nothofagus menziesii*, and clinker beech, *Nothofagus truncata*, form some thirty-seven per cent of the remaining economic forest. All the evergreens are valuable timber trees. The total cut in 1935 was 244 million cubic feet, of which rimu contributed over half. It is a strong building timber and a beautiful cabinet wood; its colour is reddish or yellow, it takes a high polish, and is very ornamental. Matai is very fine-grained, reddish in colour, and when exposed after cutting becomes so hard that it is difficult to drive nails into it. Totara and kahikatea are softer; the heart wood of totara is very durable in the ground. Kahikatea, New Zealand white pine, *Podocarpus dacrydioides*, is much used for backing veneers and plywood, and it is rather like our northern pines. Other timber trees are kawaka, *Libocedrus bidwillii*, and Westland or silver pine, *Dacrydium colensoi*. The existing forests might well be extended, for they create their own micro-climate and, if they are to be preserved for all time, the natural conditions which favour their growth must be given due consideration.

One of the most popular exotic species of tree now being planted is the well known Monterey pine, *Pinus radiata*, which flourishes on the pumice lands near Rotorua. Its growth is astonishing, being five times as fast as on its native peninsula in California. A forty-six-year-old plantation will yield as much as 207,000 board feet per acre. Douglas fir, *Pseudotsuga douglasii*, from the north-west Pacific is somewhat slower in growth, although much more rapid than in Washington or British

Columbia. Ponderosa pines are now being planted in increasing numbers, and so are the redwoods, which may in time exceed in growth that of their parent trees in the high Sierras.

It remains to be seen whether in the long run it is a good policy to sacrifice the native trees for fast-growing exotics. In monoculture there is always a grave risk of attack by parasites or pests, which may sweep the whole area. Besides, these pure stands alter the character of the country, so that it no longer enjoys the serenity or dignity of the mighty forests which once cast their magic spell over the land.

Chapter Eighteen

AUSTRALIA

Mystic, lofty, gloomy forests,
Rolling hills of God's eternal green,
Distant, blue, serrated ranges,
Mountain air all cutting, clear and keen.

Bernard O'Reilly.

WHEN I WAS A BOY, AUSTRALIA ALWAYS HELD A STRANGE fascination for me: I came of pioneering stock, and my forbears had gone to the Dominions and Colonies and had even placed whole countries on the map. Major Baker, who was a soldier by profession and a sailor by inclination, had thrice sailed round the world in his own yacht on voyages of discovery, but none of my family had ever settled in Australia. And so in my childish fancy I wondered if it would be my good fortune to go to that great continent where men could still be pioneers. "Woodcraft" and "bushcraft" were words which meant a whole lot to me, although in those days the only chance I had of playing at bushman was in the pine and beech woods which were around my home in Hampshire. My father, who had never had the opportunity of travelling farther than the South of France, had a sincere regard for what he called "Colonials"—men of our stock who had blazed the trail of overseas settlement in the great Dominions and Commonwealth of Nations. The very fact that Australia seemed so far away held out a challenge to me, and for that reason I took an inordinate delight in any story about that remote country. I was twelve years old when the Commonwealth of Australia came into being and the six colonies became known as states. But Canada was the first country to claim me, and it was not until fifteen years ago that I visited that land "way down under". It was then I realized that Australia, with its 2,974,600 square miles, was 800 square miles greater in extent than the whole of the U.S.A. From the geologists I learnt that Australia was physically the oldest of the continents. It is a great plateau

The beginning of water erosion in an abandoned field.

"Water is the source of life"—a scene in the English Lake District.

on which there are few elevations rising above 2,000 feet above
the sea. They told me that Mount Kosciusko, whose present
height is just over 7,000 feet, was once higher than Everest,
29,000 feet, but it has eroded away. The antiquity of this
country is confirmed by its trees and other vegetation, for most
of the trees are of primitive type existing elsewhere only as
fossils or in coal measures. Among the most primitive found are
the *araucarias*, monkey-puzzle trees. Eucalyptus has by far the
largest number of timber trees, for there are about 235 species,
which range in height from dwarf trees of 2 feet to giants of
326 feet. One of the tallest is the *Eucalyptus regnans* from Gipps-
land. They are known as gum trees, and their timber varies in
colour from almost white or pale cream to pink, red or brown.
Many of their barks are quite smooth and almost white, others
grey or green, while some, such as the "ribbony" gums,
Eucalyptus viminalis, have fibrous and stringy bark. Eucalyptus
is in fact a most important and widespread genus. English
names are applied loosely to different species in different districts; for instance, one of the largest eucalyptus trees known
to me is called "giant mountain ash". The particular tree I
have in mind stands about forty miles from Melbourne. I have
mislaid the measurement, but I believe it may be the largest
tree, not only in Australia, but possibly in the whole of the
British Empire.

Wattles, or acacias, contain about an equal number of
species, and they are the most characteristic flowering trees
and shrubs of the tableland bush, and their flowers are used
as an emblem of Australia. There is a wealth of flowering
trees, many of them eucalyptus, especially in Western Australia. Queensland has its tulip tree, *Stenocarpus*. Then there is
the Illawarra flame-tree, *Sterculia*, and the Western Australian
fire-tree, *Nuytsia*.

There are a large number of timbers of economic value, and
the pleasing dramatic effects of many of the ornamental, fine-
grained woods have yet to be fully appreciated. Some are
finding their way into modern buildings, not only in the towns
of their native land, but in other countries. Some have been
used most successfully in luxury liners and in railway carriages.
The New South Wales turpentine tree, *Syncarpia*, is used for

bridge piles, and eucalyptus has been used successfully in the building of harbours, for it offers considerable resistance to toledo borers. Among soft woods are the Moreton Bay pine, araucaria, the cypress pine, *Callitris*, the red cedar, *Cedrela*, or cigar-box cedar, and the red and black beans, *Dysoxylon* and *Castanospermum*. Rosewood and silky oak are popular furniture woods in the East, sandalwood in the West, and blackwood, *Acacia melanoxylon*, in Victoria and Tasmania. The beauty of many of these woods when skilfully converted has to be seen to be believed.

Unfortunately, the virgin forests from which these trees come have been exploited with too little thought for future supplies. The lands which contain such valuable trees should be worked on a sustained yield basis, so that supplies of their timbers may be available for all time. There is a danger that, when the virgin forests are felled, inferior species may take their place, for there has been a tendency to pick out the plums, or the trees that are most sought after for the beauty and usefulness of their wood, and leave the rest, with the consequence that the forest deteriorates, never to regain the natural composition which yielded those treasures. The major task of the forester is to provide his fellow men with raw materials that are indispensable and bound to become more valuable in the future. Besides that, he has the task of maintaining a tree cover on those soils which, in consequence of their physical characteristics, can be used only for forests. The way in which whole mountainsides have been deprived of their tree covering is humiliating to thoughtful people. When an earthquake razes man-made buildings to the ground, we are quick to deplore the tragedy and hasten to repair the damage; but when man destroys the finely balanced economy of Nature to satisfy his greed, we refer to it as "developing the country".

It was a tragic time for Australia when in 1788 the British Government decided to transport convicts from the crowded prisons and, later, Irish rebels in ship-loads to that continent. On these ships sailed colonists who had not been convicted of crimes, and they began to "open up" the interior. The more orderly convicts were allowed to serve them as labourers on ticket-of-leave. The foundation of convict settlements in

Australia had established the fact that Europeans could live there, and colonists reached it from the British Isles in ever-increasing numbers, till the stream became a flood when gold was discovered in the middle of the nineteenth century. In accordance with the habits and tradition of their race, the settlers demanded the right to manage their own affairs, and they did, with the disastrous results that may be witnessed in their land to-day. The inoffensive native inhabitants, who had been the forest protectors, for their wants were few, retired in rapidly dwindling numbers into the arid and tropical regions where they might escape from the invaders. Ruthless destruction of the forest began, and in their ignorance the colonists soon upset the balance of Nature. In their blindness they did not see that the forest was their friend, and treated it as an enemy to be overcome and routed. True, the pioneer took his life in his hands when he declared war on the big trees. Felling big timber is dangerous work, especially when the tops of the mighty trees are entangled with creepers. These tough vines, with which the whole jungle is interwoven, are a menace, for a falling tree may bring with it the tops of other trees yards behind in the very direction in which the axeman is jumping for cover. Again, a hollow tree is apt to upset the calculations of the most skilful axeman, and may crush him as it falls to earth in a splintered mass. Great Australian eucalyptus trees sometimes take their revenge in the moment of their fall.

"Civilized" man is, however, diabolically ingenious in the way in which he brings destruction on himself and his descendants; for, not content with felling a tree here and there to meet his needs, he must devise a skilful plan by which he can destroy as much as an acre of high forest in a fraction of the time it would take him to deal with the individual trees. His devilish device saves him much chopping, especially in hilly country where trees should never be clear-felled. This fiendish practice is known as a "drive". The axeman will lay into the trees in such a manner that each will fall on its neighbour, when the pressure from above is set off by a big "drive" tree on the uphill side of all the others. When the fate of the trees is sealed, they do not break off where they have been cut but are shattered in all directions. Beautiful timber which might have brought shelter and happiness to many generations of men is torn to splinters, while the forest echoes with shrieks and explosions, and Mother Earth, who bore the trees, trembles under the impact of their giant bodies. Tall timber may be felled over 100 acres or more at a time, and left until the end of the dry season, the ground covered to a depth of 20 or 30 feet with splintered trees and branches. The whole of this lies on a deep bed of dry leaves and rich humus, which has been gradually accumulating on the forest floor for 1,000 years. When the farmer is ready to set fire to the prepared area, he makes a torch with oil-soaked hessian and applies it along the foot of the clearing. The flames rush up the slope with a deafening roar. Dense rolling clouds of black smoke rise upwards towards the heavens. Terrific heat is generated, and the oil of the trees produce a highly inflammable gas which may quickly fill a whole valley and ignite with a deafening explosion, hurling burning trees into the air like matchwood. The heat thus generated is so fierce that the earth is severely scorched, and rocks explode as though there were an artillery bombardment. The man-made fiery hurricane gathers speed, lifting burning logs and hurtling them through the air like leaves in a whirlwind, which explains why such a forest fire will cross a valley at the speed of an express train. Soon the sun is blacked out, veiling destruction as the fire rages and sweeps on. No one who has not witnessed such a fire in Australian high forest can appreciate the speed of destruction or the amount of damage involved. Just a clearing to make a farm to grow fodder to feed cattle, which are killed to feed man. Thus man destroys the sylvan temple which God did plan and build.

When the Australian farmer uses the term "planting", he usually means sowing grass seed or farm crops. This is done after the felled forest has been burnt off. Should rain happen to fall before the "planting", the ashes form a hard surface, making it impossible for the seed to germinate, so the sowing is generally done directly the flames have died down and while many fallen trees and stumps are still burning. This task is not without its dangers, for many farmers have been severely burned.

Almost anything will grow without cultivation in this ash

from the trees that have protected and enriched the soil for a thousand years, though these methods are nothing less than despoiling the earth of the stored-up wealth of the ages. But the damage will have to be made good under threat of the extinction of humanity. Scientific forestry must become the fundamental economical factor, because it is necessary in order to assure a balance of climate and hydrography, without which a lasting civilization is impossible.

Dr. Halliday Sutherland records that since pioneering days "down under", the water table as ascertained in the sinking of wells has continuously fallen with the destruction of trees to make room for sheep and other farming. At one time there was a veritable fresh-water subterranean sea under much of Australia. The trees there sent down their roots to almost incredible depths through the subsoil to reach it, and could not otherwise have lived through long droughts. Now, even when not directly destroyed by man, they die because the water table has sunk farther than they can reach.

I have the greatest admiration for individual pioneers, both men and women, who have played their part in the drama of this old yet new continent. They have wrestled with floods, drought, fire, and disease in flocks and herds. They have faced loneliness in the great open spaces, and but for their courage and resourcefulness they would not have survived. Often in ignorance they have brought destruction upon themselves and have left behind a heritage of denuded lands. A new generation must arise who, inspired by love of the earth, will work and replenish where their fathers worked and exploited.

Fortunately, there still remain noble forests in their primitive state. Many of the eucalyptus grow so closely together that their tops are interwoven and appear to form a continuous canopy. Flying over such a forest, it looks as if it would be possible to travel for miles along the tree tops. It is slow work walking through a eucalpytus forest, and nobody who has not experience of virgin forest can appreciate the difficulty that it offers to penetration. Any forest survey in these regions is a laborious task, and one must be prepared to forgo the direct route because of the impenetrable nature of the undergrowth. The dense canopy is made all the more compact by a mass of leafy lianas which ramify among the tree tops. Under such a forest roof it might be imagined that ground growth would be suppressed and that a clean forest floor would be found; but, on the contrary, this is covered with tangled growth of evergreen plants, shrubs, and woody vines, which form a dense bush and obscure the sunlight. It is heart-breaking work to walk any distance, for it is impossible to avoid entanglement by creepers and thorns, which tear the stoutest clothes and pierce the flesh. Massive trees, felled by past cyclones, further impede progress.

Once I attempted to walk along the bole of a fallen giant to escape the surrounding jungle; but just as I was beginning to feel the relief of having defeated the murderous thorns and tangled undergrowth, the bark gave way and I dropped into a pulpy mass of decayed wood and fungus. There is no such thing as keeping a straight course in a eucalyptus forest, for to make any progress at all it is necessary to be constantly looking for diversions. Only the skilled bushman can keep his bearings and hope to arrive at his destination. There are times when even the bushman is defeated by the jungle, and it is no wonder that many dauntless ones have lost their lives when travelling under arduous conditions. But the forest has its language, and those who can read its signs may steer a desired course. The bushman knows how to find the points of the compass by the nature of the vegetation. He has observed that generally the northern and eastern slopes are matted with the luxuriant growth of lawyer and raspberry vine, while the southern slopes are covered with tree ferns and clusters of lilies. He knows, too, that the southern side of a tree is more often covered with moss and lichen, while the northern side shows a clean bole. He is helped by his knowledge of the trees and shrubs in any given area, and he knows that at the foot of the mountain ranges a certain species will bloom some weeks earlier than the same species on the higher slopes. At 1,000 feet it will be blooming, while at 2,000 feet it will still be in bud. Knowledge of the snow line may also provide a useful clue, and by such means it is possible to estimate the approximate altitude.

I shall always remember with a sense of deep satisfaction

my visits to Australian virgin bush, of which there is all too little left to meet the needs of this expanding Dominion. Although I had grown many millions of eucalyptus trees for my forest plantations in Equatorial Africa, until a few years ago I had not the chance of studying the eucalyptus family at home in their native bush. The thing that impressed me more than anything else was the dense evergreen ground-cover which protects the floor of the forest and prevents too much evaporation. Eucalyptus is a light-demanding tree, needing the ground protection which it enjoys in its native habitat. It is axiomatic to say that the amount of vegetation varies with the rainfall, but the height and quality of the timber grown may depend upon the type and density of the ground-cover. Along the eastern coast and inland to the foothills of the main range extends a well-timbered region; but as the rainfall lessens and the ground-cover changes, the character of the timber varies from the soft woods of the great coastal "brushes" to the hardwoods on the range and foothills. The coastal forests have a dense undergrowth, while on the ranges this tends to disappear, and in the foothills there are grand expanses of rich pasture land, park-like in appearance, with groups of fine trees.

In Western Australia, in contrast to Eastern Australia, there is an important forest belt on the inland side of the main range. Here may be found the popular jarrah and karri eucalyptus trees. Where the rainfall is under 20 inches, forest growth ceases and the scrubs of the plains take over. Many are the varieties of shrub eucalyptus that cover dry but otherwise fertile land. Next to this type come stunted and scattered trees with little herbage, while in the central area appear plant forms such as saltbush, *Atriplex* and *Rhagodia*, spinifex and nardoo, which provide fodder in times of drought; the last, a cryptogam, *Marsilea*, is used by the aborigines for food.

Rainfall is not the only factor controlling vegetation. Uniform climatic factors prevail over large areas, and the land relief is not, in general, enough to bring about marked changes in "local climate", so that a particular plant community often stretches unchanged for a great distance. It has been noted by those who have made a study of vegetation in the semi-arid

and arid regions of Australia that the changes of plant community within an area of uniform climate are mainly determined by edaphic or soil factors, and have to do with the
amount of soil water, or are associated with change of geological
formation. The country is divided into pastural holdings of
several hundred to over 1,000 square miles. It is difficult for
Englishmen to appreciate the extent of the Australian farms
or ranges: 640,000 acres is no mean holding! Such holdings are
called "stations" and are divided into "paddocks", usually
12,000 or 13,000 acres in extent. In the study of the forest
regions, the human factor looms large in the more settled
areas. In Victoria and Tasmania, for instance, the vegetation
has completely changed owing to interference by man. In a
few years the climax forests of *Eucalyptus regnans* which have
covered the rolling hillsides may be entirely replaced by continuous sheets of *Pteridium*, the weed which in these parts
covers worn-out potato fields.

Following the removal of the high forest with its dense
ground-covering, the rainfall tends to become less evenly distributed. When a storm breaks, run-off quickly brings erosion
to the land. Gullies are among the more spectacular results
of erosion which play havoc with hilly land, while rolling land
is rapidly ruined by the more insidious and widely destructive
process of sheet erosion. It has been demonstrated that when
gully formation has begun, the land has already lost much of
the most important element in soil fertility and stability—
namely, the water-holding capacity of the soil. This is apart
from the actual soil material which has been lost by wind
and rain. In Australia, generally speaking, the water-holding
capacity of the soil is confined mainly to a few inches on the
surface, where fresh humus formed from decaying leaves and
animal remains accumulate. Sheet erosion, by removing the
most absorbent layers, not only speeds up the run-off water
which is the chief eroding agent, but decreases the value and
shortens the period of usefulness of the rainfall. In a country
where every drop of rain is needed to maintain life, this factor
of erosion is more serious than the actual loss of soil. Hence the
clear felling of wide expanses of high forest to form sheep runs
and farms has started a vicious circle. The devastating droughts

A pond on a well-wooded estate at Dunmow, Essex.

"The forest is the mother of the rivers."

of recent years would not have been so serious fifty years ago, for much of the rain would have been held by the absorbent soil and utilized in the dry season. To-day, after years of forest destruction, an abnormal rainfall is necessary to produce the same results that might have been obtained from a moderate rainfall while the protective covering was still there. Now, a high rainfall tends to wash away more of the remaining soil than a low or moderate one. Where erosion is under way, heavy downpours of rain are an added danger, and it seems that in many parts of Australia drought conditions are past remedying. Much has been said of the Dust Bowl of the Middle West of the United States of America, but little is known of the extent or speed of water erosion and the growing desert in Australia. The wheat lands of New South Wales are the most extensively and seriously damaged areas. This is due to the fact that wheat is mostly grown on undulating land which should never have had its forest covering so drastically removed. Again, the climate conditions are more conducive to erosion. It has been observed that in Victoria, South Australia and Western Australia the rainfall tends to occur more in winter, and the intensity of individual falls is therefore not so great. In New South Wales, summer thunderstorms are more frequent and more intense, with greater ensuing damage. The obvious remedy is to reafforest all hilly country and make pastures of undulating land, establishing frequent shelter-belts of forest trees, which would be a valuable asset to every station. The reclamation of desert and arid regions would provide work for tens of thousands of planters who might be trained in the particular technique required for such a vast and difficult undertaking. The effort to study the arid vegetation at Koonamore under the supervision of the University of Adelaide on a sheep station of over 1,000 square miles, with an average rainfall of only 8·45 inches, will be watched with interest.

Research is needed to discover what species can best be grown in shelter-belts in such arid regions. The more arid parts of the Soviet Union may contain a number of plants of various types which would be of service in the work of land reclamation in Australia. However, there is no doubt that hundreds of useful trees and shrubs for desert planting might be found

among the 147 natural orders that are represented in the
native flora. The forest is the most useful servant of man. Not
only does it sustain and regulate the streams, moderate the
winds, prevent droughts, and beautify the land, but it also
supplies wood, the most widely used of all natural products.
Its uses are numberless, and the demands that are made upon
it by mankind are numberless also. It is essential for the well-
being of mankind that their demands be met; but the length
of time required for the growth of a forest shows conclusively
that it was never destined in the order of Nature for the ex-
clusive use of a single generation. Even though great cities may
be built from the profit resulting from the exploitation of virgin
lands and forests, Nature will exact her payment. If the Dust
Bowl of the Middle West was the price exacted for the sky-
scrapers of New York, Australians may well ask themselves
what the bill will be for theirs.

Chapter Nineteen

SOUTH AMERICAN VISTA

For Nature ever faithful is
To such as trust her faithfulness.
When the forest shall mislead me,
When the night and morning lie,
When sea and land refuse to feed me,
'Twill be time enough to die; . . .

Emerson.

SOUTH AMERICA IS LINKED WITH AUSTRALIA THROUGH HER trees, even though the countries are divided by the greatest expanse of ocean in the world. A tree tribe which spans the Southern Seas is one of the most primitive gymnosperms: they are the *Araucarineae*. They were flourishing at the same time as the giant reptiles who laid their eggs on dry land and were independent of water for breeding purposes. In a similar way, the members of this tribe of conifers with a hard-coated seed depended on air and wind rather than water for their reproduction, so there must have been a land bridge at one time, or maybe the continent of Mu linked Australia to Chile. There are about ten species of araucaria, inhabitants of South America, Australia, New Guinea, New Hebrides, New Caledonia, Norfolk Island, and New Zealand. The long mountain ranges of the Andes are covered with mixed evergreen forests, dominated by conifers. Beginning at 36° South latitude is *Araucaria imbricata*, now so well known in Great Britain and other parts of the world. Unlike its New Zealand cousin, the giant kauri pine, it will stand frost. Although treated as a curiosity in European parks and gardens, in Kenya it has been successfully planted as a forest. These tall evergreen trees are distinguished from the other conifers by having a single ovule on a simple scale. The araucarias are unlike any other tree in the world. How can I describe these lordly trees, which tower to heights from 100 to 160 feet? Their straight, cylindrical stems lift their broad umbrella-shaped crowns of very crowded branches high over the heads of lesser forest denizens. Their bark is very rough, and divided into curious scales: it is a perfect child's puzzle of slabs of different sizes with five or six distinct sides to each, all fitted together as neatly as a honeycomb. The branches are at first very spreading, and in young or isolated individuals they persist for a long time. In the forests they generally fall off, leaving only their crowns, which are a striking sight.

Their leaves are all of one kind, spirally crowded on the branches, rigid, ovate-lanceolate in shape, with a sharp point at the apex. The leaf is slightly concave on the upper surface, glabrous, and shining bright green in colour. If a still closer examination is made with the help of a lens or microscope, it will be seen that each leaf is marked with longitudinal lines and has many stomata on both surfaces. The margins of a leaf are cartilaginous. The leaves of this curious tree persist for ten to fifteen years, and only begin to wither during the latter part of their life. For a long time after a leaf has fallen, its remains may be seen on trunk and branches as narrow transverse ridges.

The male flowers are catkins, almost cylindrical in shape. They are either solitary or two to six in a cluster, and are erect, 3 to 5 inches in length, yellow in colour, composed of densely packed anther scales, the tips of which are sharply pointed and recurved; there are from six to nine pollen sacks. The extraordinary thing is that the male flowers frequently remain intact on the tree for several years, though generally in Europe they appear only in spring, the pollen escaping in June or July. The female flowers are ovoid in shape, and one only is born at terminal shoots. It, too, is erect, about 3 inches long, and is composed of numerous wedge-shaped scales which terminate in long, narrow, brittle points. After fertilization, the cone takes two years to ripen, though three months after its fertilization the seeds are fully mature; there are about 300 seeds in a cone. Nature has been very cautious with the Chilian Araucarias, for she has not only protected the trees with formidable armour, but even the fertilizing apparatus and the cones themselves are covered by a thick brown coat.

It is interesting to make a close study of the seedling. The cotyledons are two in number, and on germination remain below the soil enclosed in the seed. The caulicule, to which the cotyledons are attached, is thick, fleshy, and carrot-shaped, serving as a store of nutritious food for the plant after that of the cotyledons is exhausted; it is directed downward into the soil, and terminates in a long, slender, fibrous root, which gives off a few lateral rootlets. The plumule, the portion of the axis with its accompanying leaves, which is formed in the embryo prior to generation, protrudes between the stalks of the cotyledons, speedily becomes erect, and develops into the young stem, which bears leaves similar in shape to those of the adult plant. Some time after the stem has grown above ground, the cotyledons wither away, the ends of their stalks being visible on the upper part of the caulicule. At the end of the first season, the stem is 4 or 5 inches long and bears alternate leaves about $\frac{3}{4}$ inch long, gradually increasing in size from below upwards, and a crowded tuft at the summit, a pattern of things to come. The lower end of the stem is reddish, with leaves small and scale-like. The fusiform caulicule, about 1 inch in length, is continued below into a root 8 or 9 inches long.

Now what about the sex of this remarkable tree? The araucaria is usually dioecious, the trees being either male or female. There are some who believe that there is a difference in the habit of the two sexes, but a careful study has shown that araucarias differ remarkably in habit and no inference can be drawn as to sex from the habit or character or from the growth of an individual. Monoecious trees, as is the case in nearly every dioecious species, are of exceptional and very rare occurrence. Augustine Henry noted that these occurred at Bicton, the seat of Lord Clinton, and in the gardens of Lytchett Manor, near Poole, belonging to Sir John Lees, Bart.

This curious tree was discovered about 1780 by a Spaniard, Don Francisco Dendariarena, who was employed by the Spanish Government to examine the trees in the country of the Araucanos in the south of Chile, with the object of finding out those trees whose timber was best suited for ship-building. His account of its discovery, as quoted by Lambert, is as follows:

N

"In September 1782 I left my companion, Don Hippolito Ruiz, and visited the mountains named Caramaviva and Nahuelbuta, belonging to the Llanistha, Peguen, and Araucano Indians. Amongst many plants, which were the result of my two months' excursion, I found in flower and fruit the tree I am about to describe.

"The chain or cordillera of the Andes offers to the view in general a rocky soil, in parts wet and boggy, on account of the abundance of rain and snow which falls in these regions, similar to many provinces in Spain. There are to be seen large forests of this tree, which rises to the amazing height of one hundred and fifty feet, its trunk quite straight and without knots, ending in a pyramid formed of horizontal branches which decrease in length gradually towards the top, is covered with a double bark, the inner five or six inches thick, fungus, tenacious, porous, and light, from which, as from almost all other parts, flows resin in abundance; the outer is of nearly equal thickness, resembling cork cleft in various directions, and equally resinous with the inner."

It has been suggested that the district mentioned by him is not really part of the Andes at all, but a close range separated from the Andes by a wide track of low country, mostly covered with forest. The tree was first fully described by the Abbé Molina, who called it *Pinus Araucania*. Ruiz and Pabon, who explored parts of Chile soon afterwards, sent specimens to Europe to a Frenchman named Dombey, which were described by Lamarck under the name of *Dombeya chilensis*; but the genetic name he gave cannot stand, because it was previously used for a genus of *Sterculiaceae*.

In 1795 Captain Vancouver, after whom Vancouver Island was named, visited the coast of Chile accompanied by Archibald Menzies, who was medical doctor to the expedition and who procured some seeds which he sowed on board ship and succeeded in bringing home as living plants. These he gave to Sir Joseph Banks, who planted one of them in his own garden at Spring Grove and sent the remaining five plants to Kew. One of these, after being kept in the greenhouse till

about 1806, was planted out on what is now called Lawn L,
and was at first protected during winter by a frame covered
with mats; here it grew for many years and attained a height of
12 feet in 1836, but eventually died in the autumn of 1892 at
the age of nearly 100 years.

It did not, however, become common in cultivation till the
celebrated botanical traveller, William Lobb, who was sent to
South America by the well-known nursery firm of Veitch, sent
home in 1844 a good supply of seeds which produced most of
the finest trees now in England. In their native habitat they
grow in scattered groups on the cliffs at an elevation of 3,000
to 4,000 feet, or scattered among coigue or beech trees, *Fagus
dombeyi*, and higher up in a forest among niere and another
beech, *Fagus antarctica*. With them are about four podocarp
pines, *Fitzroya patagonica*, and in the extreme south quite extensive forests of at least two species of incense cedar. Remnants
of these forests extend northward into Peru and across the
Andes into Argentina. They are at their best in boggy valleys,
where the ground underneath is enlivened with purple and
pink everlasting peas, beautiful terrestrial orchids, and other
plants. They do not always have such flat tops as those of
Brazil, but are more domed, like those in Queensland. It is a
wild and rugged country in which they thrive amid huge grey
boulders covered with moss, and here and there a profusion of
wild flowers. They look out over the snowy cones of the Cordillera, which pierce their way through the long line of mist
and often hide the nearer mountains from sight. On the wind-
swept ridges at 6,000 feet the araucarias are more stunted and
have a different habit of growth. The geographical range of the
tree is a very limited one, extending only from Antuco in
about latitude 38° 40′, to latitude 40° in the Cordillera, and
on the coast range from about latitude 38° 30′ to an unknown
point, probably not south of about latitude 41°. The soil on
which they grow is mostly of volcanic origin, sometimes covered
with deep vegetable mould, but more usually dry and rocky.
The climate, though warm and dry in the months of Decem-
ber, January, and February, is cold and wet in winter. There
are two types of araucaria forests, one of which is characteristic
of the rainy coast mountain range of Nahuelbuta and the west

side of the Andes on the Cordillera of Pemehue; the other is peculiar to the drier plateaux of the Argentine territory on the east side of the watershed. In the museum of Santiago there are geological evidences of the existence of a former period of araucaria as far north as the Puna of Atacama.

Chile is divided by Nature into three separate zones, each with its distinctive climate and industrial interests. First the northern zone, which consists largely of sandy, arid deserts, and is also a region holding vast mineral wealth, particularly copper and nitrate of soda. Then comes the central region, comprising fertile agricultural valleys, traversed and watered by numerous rivers running from east to west. There are also active industrial districts. Lastly, the third of the zones, where the central valley lies and the coastal range is transformed into a vast archipelago—here sheep and cattle are raised and virgin forests abound. Comparing these three topographical features of Chile with those of other parts of the world, it may be said that the northern region is much like the desert sections of North Africa, both in colouring and configuration; the central zone like the State of California; and the southern zone similar to Norway.

General Arthur Goodall Wavell, grandfather of Field-Marshal Lord Wavell, is conspicuous among those who helped the country towards independence. His vision embraced political co-operation of all nations of the hemisphere, and his life was dedicated to the welfare of the peoples of Latin America. It is not surprising that his grandson is writing a glorious page in the history of the world's struggle for the principles of liberty and justice.

Speaking at the World Forestry Charter Luncheon held in London for representatives of the Diplomatic Corps at the Dorchester Hotel on April 9, 1946, the Chilean Ambassador, Señor Don Manuel Bianchi, said:

"For the second time it is my privilege to attend the gathering of the Men of the Trees, the Society founded in 1922 by Mr. Richard St. Barbe Baker.

"At last year's meeting a plan was submitted for a World Charter for Forestry, containing many useful suggestions for

the general preservation of woods, the reafforestation of uncultivated land, the employment of large stretches of water,
legislation for the prevention of forest fires, the creation of
National Parks and improved education in forestry, etc.

"I passed on to the Chilean Government the Society's
Memorandum, and am happy to tell you that the idea of
such a World Charter for Forestry is warmly welcomed in
my country. Chilean forestry legislation is in many respects
identical with that suggested in the Memorandum in question. Chile, especially in the southernmost part, is one of
the most richly wooded countries in the world, and my
Government, aware of the present-day need of timber for
the reconstruction of the devastated zones of Europe, does
everything possible to increase and preserve this richness.

"I offer my congratulations to Mr. St. Barbe Baker for his
initiative in putting forward the idea of a World Charter for
Forestry, which I hope will be realized in the very near
future."

Nominally, Chile, with its 200,000 square miles, has a total
forest area of 60,000 square miles, but actually there is only
about 8,000 square miles of what would be termed commercial forest.

Flying over from the Argentine I was struck by the tre-
mendous amount of forest that was being felled. Large tracts
had been cleared to make farms, and I was reminded of the
similar devastation I had seen in New Zealand. Little information is available about erosion in South America, for it is still
in the advancing, pioneering stage. The cream of fertility is
being fast extracted from the Argentine pampas, but so far
only the far-sighted are concerned with the trend of exploitation.
For many days I travelled across the continent from Buenos
Aires to the Andes, and I became alarmed at the extensive
removal of forests. The soil fertility in the Argentine is known
to be decreasing, on account of the continuous removal of
animal products and the neglect to use manures and natural
compost. The classical example of mountain terracing in Peru
stands as a lesson to modern soil miners. The latest reports
from the Argentine state that there are approximately 193,000

square miles of forest, or seventeen per cent. Felling is permitted only in the case of trees which have reached a state of maturity, and since the Forestry Directorate assumed its functions one of its primary considerations has been the reafforestation of cut-over Government forests by the transplanting of trees from nurseries or by direct sowing. These operations are now being put into effect for the first time under the supervision of Demonstration Forestry Stations.

As I sailed up the Plata, our ship scraped her bottom on the silt which had come down the river and its tributaries, not only from the felled forest areas of the Argentine, but from the lands of Paraguay and Uruguay and Brazil. Paraguay, with its 162,000 square miles, is said to contain 43,500 square miles of forest, and Uruguay, which is 72,000 square miles in extent, has a total forest area of 2,300 square miles, or just over three per cent of the total land area. Bolivia, with 514,000 square miles, has 197,000 square miles, or thirty-seven per cent of the total land area. But wherever I went I saw that severe inroads were being made into virgin forests, and in my opinion I nowhere saw large-scale reafforestation. The cause of the silting up of the mouth of the Plata is the denudation of the hinterland which is drained by this great river and its tributaries. The entrance to the fine harbour of Buenos Aires is only kept open at a great cost by dredging. A far-sighted policy would support large-scale reafforestation of all steep land and mountainsides, and plant up the banks of all rivers with species to fix the soil and prevent water erosion. But this would call for the concerted action of all those countries I have mentioned. National feuds and rivalry would have to be sunk in this great task. The fertility of these lands and the preservation of their waterways can be maintained at no less a cost than close international co-operation.

Much of the land is a natural domain of forests. At the first World Forestry Charter Luncheon held in London in 1945, and over which Lord Sempill presided, the Argentine Ambassador, Dr. Don Miguel Carcano, gave a valuable lead when he stressed the vital importance of forestry in his country. He recognized the necessity of planting both to safeguard the valuable timber resources of the Argentine and to prevent soil erosion. His Excellency described many of the most interesting trees, and mentioned one that is as hard as steel. He said that they knew how to cut it, but so far they had not discovered the silvicultural treatment required for regenerating it. He suggested that it presented a problem to the World Forestry Committee.

The largest and most valuable evergreen forest in the whole of the southern hemisphere is that of the Paraná pine, *Araucaria angustifolia*, which is situated on the east watershed of the Paraná River in Brazil and extends into Paraguay and Argentina. Paraná pine is the Brazilian araucaria. It grows in mixed tropic and semi-tropic forests on the cooler elevated highlands forming the upper story of the forest and shading a great variety of lower-growing hardwood trees. The total area of Paraná pine has been estimated at 300,000 square miles, with commercial stands covering 100 million acres, meaning perhaps a total stand of 40 billion cubic feet. It is an excellent softwood timber, taking the place of northern deals, and it is reported to be good for pulp-making. With this pine are two podocarps, these three species being the only conifers so far found in Brazil. Growing in their native habitat, these trees form a really beautiful type of forest. They are like great umbrellas opened out to shade the lesser forest denizens. Their trunks are straight, and the older trees are free of branches below their widespreading crowns. Trees have been found up to 8 feet in diameter, but 3 feet is more usual, and logs 60 to 80 feet in length may be considered average. The proximity of the Paraná pine forests to the great rivers Paraná and Uruguay and their tributaries makes logging easy, and at the rate of exploitation it will not be so long before the virgin forest has been exhausted. The fast-growing towns commit terrible aggression upon them.

The nut-like seed of the Paraná pine is the largest and most delicious of all the edible conifer seeds. It is as large as a chestnut and is gathered by the natives and Italian settlers, who boil them, for they make an excellent food. They are common in the markets of the cities of southern Brazil.

The total forest area of Brazil, a country of over 3,000,000 square miles, is reputed to be 1,395,000 square miles, or

24·7 per cent of the total land area. Only 155,000 square miles consists of conifers, and the great majority is tropical rain forest. The country, which is the largest state of South America, lies almost wholly within the tropics and is still in great part unexplored and unsettled. The warm south equatorial currents sweep the coast and pass up through the Caribbean Sea into the Gulf of Mexico. These, the greatest tropical forests in the world, are drained by the mighty Amazon and its tributaries. There are large areas of flood plains and swamps, heavily wooded and only sparsely inhabited by Indians. But Brazil really possesses three great river systems, for there are large areas drained by the Plata and São Francisco. The Amazon and its tributaries drain fully half of the country. To the east of the Madeira, these tributaries are tableland rivers, broken by rapids and only navigable for comparatively short distances. West of the Madeira they are lowland rivers, sluggish, bordered by extensive flood plains and navigable for long distances. The La Plata system drains nearly one-fifth of the country through its three branches, the Paraguay, Paraná, and Uruguay. The first of these is a lowland river easily navigated for a long distance, while the other two are tableland rivers, full of obstructions and without free outlets for their upper level navigation. The São Francisco is a tableland river, flowing north-east between the Goyaz and maritime mountains, and then breaking through the latter, south-east to the Atlantic. Its tributaries are comparatively short, and nearly disappear along the lower river in the region of slight rainfall. It is not freely navigated because of the Paulo Affonso Falls. The other coast rivers are generally short.

The climate of Brazil has great variations, the lowlands of the Amazon and the major part of the coast being hot, humid, and unhealthy, while the tablelands and some districts of the coast, swept by the trade winds, are temperate and healthy. There are large areas subject to serious droughts, but for the greater part the vegetation of Brazil and Amazonia proper is luxuriant and varied. The vast rain forests of the Amazon contain hundreds of species of trees draped and festooned by climbing plants and orchids, and yield many beautiful and attractive woods. Rosewood was familiar as a decorative wood throughout the last century. Its popularity began with the Empire period, and in the early days of Queen Victoria's reign, used both solid and in veneer, it was employed in the best cabinet work. The Bahia timber stood first for quality, while that from Rio, though less well-marked and figured, produced both larger and better pieces free from defect. It has remained in favour more in France and America than in the United Kingdom; this may have been partly due to the difficulty experienced in obtaining good, sound wood of a sufficiently large size to yield good veneer or panels. The peroba-rosa, *Aspidosperma peroba*, is of a pale rose-colour with some darker streaks. It has a very hard, firm, close-grained texture. In appearance it resembles the East African pencil cedar, but is very much harder. Zebrawood, *Astronium fraxinifolium*, is, as its name implies, characteristically striped. Brazilwood, *Caesalpinia echinata*, is of a rich bright red colour and is mostly used as a dye-wood, while the best pieces are selected for turning and for violin bows. It is outstandingly the best wood for this last purpose, and, although many different kinds of timber have been tried, there is nothing that will yield the same result as the *Pernambuco* or Brazilwood, and many players will use no other kind on account of the peculiarly strong resilient spring only to be found in this wood. When planed, it has a bright metallic, lustrous surface and shows fine, snake-like ripple marks. Santa maria, *Calophyllum brasiliense*, is pale reddish in colour, is moderately hard, and has a fine straight grain, is easily worked, and is sometimes used in place of mahogany. Kingwood, *Dalbergia sp.*, is of a rich violet-brown, shading sometimes almost to black, and streaked with varying lighter and darker markings of golden-yellow. It has a bright lustre and will finish with a smooth surface. It is always beautiful as a cabinet wood, and as it tones with age its value is greatly enhanced. Brazilian tulip wood, *Physocalymma scaberrimum*, is fresh red in colour, streaked with deeper red and light yellow stripes. It is dense and hard and very liable to split after being sawn, but it is a favourite wood in the composition of French pieces of furniture, especially of the Empire period, and is still used for bandings and ornamental inlay work. Peroba branca, *Paratecoma peroba*, is light greyish-yellow in colour. It attains large dimensions and is fit for use in architecture, for furniture, and generally in the domestic arts. The tree is of straight growth and is even stronger than teak, *Tectona grandis*. At one time Brazilian ironclads were built of it. It is a valuable timber and should find many important uses. Quebracho, *Schinopsis lorentzii*, is one of the best-known woods both in Brazil and the Argentine. It is very hard and heavy and is exceedingly dense, with close grain, and of a deep red colour. It is principally used for railway sleepers, immense quantities of which are exported. It is also felled to a great extent for the manufacture of charcoal. Swietenia is one of the *Meliaceae*, which might be termed the mahogany family. The swietenia trees themselves have leaves which recall those of an ash in design though not in shape. It is not only one of the most important furniture woods, but is used for pattern-making, and many key industries depend upon ample supplies of this wood. Because of its decorative qualities, it is very much sought after in furniture-making and has a unique reputation on account of its beautiful grain and markings.

Besides producing valuable timber, the great forest of the Amazon also yields rubber, and the well-known Pará is the native home of the tree which is now grown so extensively in plantations. The popular Brazilian nut is from a forest tree, and great quantities are collected for export.

In supporting my proposal for a World Charter for Forestry in 1946, Senhor Dr. J. J. Moniz de Aragão, Ambassador of Brazil, said:

"I must confess to a certain diffidence in addressing you at this delightful ceremony of to-day, as my ignorance of forestry is—alas!—very great.

"In one respect, however, I appreciate the reason for having been invited to speak on the subject of trees.

"As you are no doubt aware, Brazil represents, to-day, by far the largest extent of forest of any country in the world. With the exception of a clearly defined area in the South of Brazil, where the araucaria or umbrella pine flourishes, all of this vast expanse is covered by hardwoods of the most varied kind. Contrary to most other timber areas, Brazilian hardwood forests enjoy the peculiarity of having no stands of timber of any *one* variety exclusively—but represent a veritable U.N.O. of dozens of species living together in perfect amity and security.

"Now this, although a grave disadvantage from the angle of economic exploitation, has this recompense as seen from the point of view of this Society, that the destruction of our forests is much less than it might otherwise have been, and, in fact, only occurs when land has to be cleared for the cultivation of coffee, cotton, sugar or grain. This does not mean that many of our noble virgin forests have not been carelessly sacrificed, but it can be said, on the whole, that relatively small inroads have been made in the great kingdom of primeval forest, where life, as it existed in the dawn of history, still continues unchanged.

"How long this state of affairs can last, is hard to say. Brazil is the fourth-largest country in the world in extent, with a population approximately that of the United Kingdom.

"Owing to the political state of Europe, not only during the war, but for a considerable number of years before, immigration into Brazil was severely reduced. Now that hostilities have ceased, my country intends to embark on a vast scheme of developing our hinterland to a degree previously unknown. But no longer will immigration be uncontrolled, but scientifically planned.

"This implies that wanton destruction of our great trees will not be permitted unchecked. Brazil will greatly benefit by this far-sighted programme, which, by sparing the trees wherever possible, will, above all, prevent land erosion, that inevitable fate of land laid waste by indiscriminate destruction of forests, and will prevent vast fertile areas of my country being transformed, as is the case in so many other lands, into a hopeless and sterile desert.

"In Brazil, timber is extensively used as fuel on certain railways, for which, nearly always, second-growth trees are utilized. For the last twenty years it has been the practice of these railways to plant the land adjoining their tracks with vast extents of the eucalyptus tree, which has the advantage of growing with great rapidity and transforming mosquito-ridden swamps into healthy areas, and to utilize the timber at the end of ten years for fuel and for sleepers. I believe I am right in stating that these eucalyptus plantations in Brazil constitute the largest stands of this timber in the world.

"With the rapidly expanding iron industry in the State of Minas Gerais, wood is at present being extensively transformed into charcoal for the reduction of our iron ore into pig-iron. Here, too, our Government have taken immediate steps for the reafforestation of lands thus denuded.

"To conclude, I feel pride in being able to say that my country is fully alive to the ideals and precepts of this Society, to the benefits of mankind in general, the importance of which cannot be too strongly stressed in any land thus favoured by nature. To its dye-woods Brazil owes its very name."

The Spanish republic of Peru, with a coast-line of 1,400 miles along the Pacific, has an area of 522,700 square miles with a total forest area of 270,000 square miles, or 51·6 per cent of the total land area. The Montaña is the region of tropical forest within the basin of the River Amazon, including the wooded slopes of the eastern watershed of the Andes, which may be called the sub-tropical portion of the Montaña. This is the region of the coca, *Erythroxylon coca*, from which cocaine is made. I have found the bush growing on plains in the Highlands of Kenya. My carriers would sometimes chew the leaf when they were fatigued on a long *safari*, and they found it mildly stimulating. From the forest-covered plains come india-rubber, sarsaparilla, the Peruvian mahogany, and a great variety of useful and ornamental timber. The Sierra of Peru is the original home of the potato. Its lofty heights also produce several other edible roots and the grain called quinoa, while splendid crops of maize are grown in the valleys. Early agriculture in Peru was particularly notable for the remarkable systems of terraces that it produced. As soon as the forest land was cleared for cultivation, it was found necessary to throw up small earth barriers to catch the soil washed down from above, and each year, as more soil came down, the barriers had to be raised and lengthened until in the course of centuries a complete terrace system came into existence. This ancient system might, in many of the newer countries where forest-clearing is taking place, be supplemented by a pattern of protective tree belts, including leguminous species which, while fixing the soil with its root system, would at the same time impregnate the ground with nitrogen.

Ecuador may be regarded as consisting of three divisions: the lowlands west of the Andes, the mountainous plateau of the interior, and the less elevated country to the east. Where the rain-clouds of the Pacific are caught, the gorges of the western spurs of mountains and most of the land is covered with luxurious, tropical vegetation. Valuable trees and plants wage bloodless conflict in a battle of species for existence against the stifling embraces of creepers, mosses, parasitic plants, and gorgeous orchids. Of the total land area of 167,600 square miles, 90,000 square miles, or 53·6 per cent, is forest. The world was first indebted to the province of Loja for cinchona bark, from which quinine is made.

The great Republic of Colombia, occupying the north-west corner of the South American continent from the frontiers of Ecuador, Peru, Brazil, and Venezuela to those of Panama, with 500 miles of coast on the Caribbean Sea and 600 on the Pacific, has a land area estimated at 462,000 square miles, of which 231,000 square miles—fifty per cent of the total land area of the country—is classed as forest.

Addressing the World Forestry Charter Luncheon, Señor Don Arturo Martinez Herrera, Colombian Embassy, said:

"I am here to-day as a mere substitute, circumstances beyond his control having prevented our Ambassador from being present at this gathering. The few remarks I am about to make have, however, been the subject of conversations between us.

"We share to the full your conviction that the problem of food shortages, which now confronts the world and threatens to become permanent, needs something more than the creation of U.N.R.R.A. and moral exhortations, and that in no other field of human activity is co-operation so necessary.

"It is therefore, with a deep sense of our responsibilities towards this movement, that we join you to-day.

"We in Colombia are confronted with a problem which, in the present state of our financial and technical resources, seems beyond our strength. Lack of statistics and the absence of periodical surveys have for a long time veiled the threatening devastation of our lands. But we are feeling the full blast of the drought that from our bare mountains and nude valleys is sweeping away our agriculture. We learn how, in one of our countries alone, 200 hectares of arable land are daily washed away by our father river on its way to the sea; how the river which provides water for one of our largest cities has been reduced to a third of its volume in the last ten years; how injudicious colonization has led to the deforestation of the heads of our rivers, in order to bring the land under cultivation. In one specific case we have spent considerable sums during the last seven years to reforest the head of a river which provides the water supply of another important city and irrigates one of our richest valleys, besides providing a waterway through which trade and commerce have flowed in the past. And additional expenditure has been necessary for resettling in more suitable areas the people who were unwisely allowed to settle in such vital places.

"I think that, bearing in mind our experience and the waste understandable in such vast areas, our legislation, if not altogether effective, now aims at stemming the speed of the destruction. A law passed in 1938 makes it compulsory for each landowner to plant for every hectare [1 hectare = 2·4711 acres] in his possession, ten trees whose wood may be used for building purposes. The same law establishes that whenever new land is granted, trees may be felled for the use of their timber, but each tree felled must be replaced with one of its own kind. We have in every county-town or city with a revenue of over 1,000,000 pesos, a special tax known as the 'park and tree tax', the amounts collected to be applied to the building and improvement of parks (especially children's parks), and the planting of trees in squares, streets and roads. And the majority of our cities offer a beautiful spectacle of streets, even those congested with traffic being lined throughout their length with lovely trees.

"You will understand, of course, that in a country such as ours, with great expanses of unoccupied lands, sparse population and poor technical means, it is a very difficult task indeed to protect our forests and to enforce existing legislation.

"Our men and women have begun to realize, however, the magnitude of the problem, and the tree has been recognized again as a faithful and useful friend. There is a sort of reconciliation between man and forest. The character of our forests is no longer, as Aldous Huxley said, appalling, or fundamentally and utterly inimical to intruding man. Nor is, as he adds, 'the life of those vast masses of swarming vegetation alien to the human spirit and hostile to it'.

"Of course many years will pass and more good earth will be lost before we achieve the reafforestation scheme of the Scottish Highlands or our schools provide millions of trees, as in Australia. Our problem is great, but no problem is beyond human ingenuity and human co-operation, and we welcome this opportunity to draw on the common pool of knowledge provided by this association.

"We look to you for guidance on common principles and common measures. Show us what you have done; enlighten us with your experience; advise us in our technical difficulties, so that we may all go forward together in a great cause."

The United States of Venezuela has a total land area of 398,600 square miles, almost half of which is forest. It is a land of mountains and valleys in the west and north, of lower mountains and wooded hills in the south, of llanos between the Orinoco and the northern ranges, and of lake, swamp, and forest in the north-west. The llanos occupy a quarter of the country lying between the Orinoco and northern chains, and are mostly undulating plains of long grass, broken by low plateaux or mesas and by numerous clumps of trees and belts of forest which rise out of the savanna. The llanos north of the lower Orinoco towards Paria peninsula are dreary, sand-swept, and treeless, except along the shallow water courses. Vegetation in the Tierra Caliente is luxuriant beyond description. The forests are dense with noble trees, and yield gums, balsams, dye-woods, india-rubber, sarsaparilla, quinine, vanilla, and tanka beans. Where water fails in the low-lying valleys, cactus forms take the place of other vegetation.

Partridge wood, *Caesalpinia granadillo*, often formerly employed in the Brazils for ship-building, is known in British dockyards as cabbage-wood, and is now principally used for walking sticks or umbrella and parasol sticks, and in cabinet work and turning. The wood is close, heavy, and generally straight in the grain.

The Venezuelan boxwood is famous; it is beautifully grown, and attains a height of 70 feet, practically free from a single knot throughout its length. At the extreme top the tree branches out into a tuft of foliage. Besides being used for inlay work and bandying in cabinets, for handles of all kinds of tools, for brush-backs, mathematical instruments and rules, barometer-backs, and for many kinds of turned work, in France and Germany it is now extensively employed for making small combs.

British Guiana is the home of the famous greenheart, *Ocotea rodiaei*, from which salmon, trout, and other fishing rods are made. A fine sample of greenheart can be made into an exceedingly small top joint for such a rod, and will bend to an extraordinary extent without breaking. The colour is of a pale yellowish-green, while sometimes it is quite dark with brown and black streaks. The black greenheart is considered to be the best. It is largely used for piles for sea jetties and docks; although not entirely immune, the wood is partially proof against the attack of the teredo worm.

The total forest area of British Guiana is 78,700 square miles, or eighty-eight per cent of the total land area. That of Dutch Guiana is 48,000 square miles, or ninety per cent, and of French Guiana 24,000 square miles, or seventy per cent. One of the best-known timbers from French Guiana is angélique, *Dicorynia paraensis*. The wood is of a reddish-brown colour, clean and even in the grain, moderately hard, tough, strong, elastic, and not difficult to work, although it does not cleave readily. It has been said that it does not rot in water, that it is durable, and that it is proof against attacks from many insects to which other timber is prone. The mora wood, *Mora excelsa*, is found both in British and Dutch Guiana. My old Reader in Forestry, Herbert Stone, used to say that it is more durable than teak. He recognized three varieties: the red, the white, and mora-bucquia; this last, however, is not considered to be durable. The wood of mora proper is a yellowish-brown colour, and contains in its pores an oily and glutinous substance which probably contributes to its durability. It is of close texture, and has occasionally a twist or waviness in the fibre which imparts to the logs possessing it a beautifully figured appearance. In its native forest it stands out conspicuous among the other trees. Sometimes an old tree may be seen festooned with creepers, the wild fig-tree often rears itself from one of the thick branches at its top, and when its fruit is ripe the birds will resort to it for nourishment. An undigested seed, passing through the body of a bird which had perched on the mora, grew to the fig tree which found itself in this elevated position. The sap of the mora tree nourished it, and in time maybe it would itself become host to other species of vines. Such creepers soon vegetate and bear fruit, and in their turn attract other birds, who deposit further seeds—and so the old mora tree becomes an unwilling host to numbers of parasitic creepers which trail themselves along his branches and intertwine him with neighbouring trees. Such is life in the Guiana forests. A vine which the wood-cutters call the bush-rope, on account of its use in hauling out the heaviest timber, is conspicuous in the forests of Demerara. Sometimes it may be seen almost as thick as a man's body, twisting itself like a corkscrew around the tallest tree and rearing its head high above the top of its host. They will sometimes throw out aerial roots which in time reach the ground and pass on or entangle other trees, joining tree and tree and branch and branch together. Other parasitic creepers will throw out shoots in all directions, forming a veritable mat of tangled lianas. Often a tree uprooted by a whirlwind will be caught in the cat's cradle thus formed and

o

be held for years 'twixt earth and sky. It may take a new lease of life and throw up fresh shoots at the junction of root and trunk, while all along the sloping trunk will appear fresh shoots, which in their turn grow erect in their search for light. It is said that the topmost branch of an old dead mora tree, when naked with age or struck by lightning, is the favourite resort of the toucan, where he sits yelping far out of range of the gun of the fowler. He is a deep-forest bird, feeding on the fruits and seeds of the forest, his mate laying eggs in hollow trees, which he serves by helping to distribute their seeds for regeneration. Many other birds play their part in helping to perpetuate the remarkable forests of this great hemisphere.

It is devoutly to be wished that the comparatively extensive tree cover of South America will be preserved, for it is a unique possession in our world of ruthless exploitation of woodland wealth, and should be maintained in the interest of the human race. Speaking broadly, it has never happened in history that sylvan economy has been maintained. The story of the rise and fall of past civilizations has coincided with the exploitation of the forests—each rose to their peak, then declined as green forest mantle was lost. Unaware of their dependence upon trees, they failed to preserve a reasonable soil-cover, and so exposed their society to the fall which must come as the result of such ignorant negligence. The world is slow to recognize the need for great forests close to large centres of population. Legislation seems powerless to guarantee protection or ensure the future existence of the human race. It would seem that nothing short of a universal spiritual regeneration will suffice to change the heart of man and enable him to recognize the law of return and the reasonable demands made by the Creator.

Chapter Twenty

TREES OR FAMINE

The tree of the field is man's life.
Deut. 20: 19.

T HE STORY OF THE FORESTS OF THE WORLD IS AN ENDLESS one, and it is quite impossible to tell it in a single volume. It begins long before man existed on this planet, and it will end only if man fails to recognize his dependence upon tree-growth for his existence. The fundamental history of civilization is the history of the soil and its cover. Civilization is a race between education and catastrophe. We have travelled far in our survey and have already witnessed the disastrous effects which follow the removal of the essential covering. We have seen that it is possible to conserve and replenish the forests of the world and maintain an adequate standard of living in all countries, provided the people unite in this task. The earth is a great entail, and it belongs as much to those who come after as to ourselves.

Travelling up from the South American continent, we glimpse the equatorial and tropical forest regions of Central America, where Aztec and earlier civilizations left stone sculpture and monumental remains now covered in the dark recesses of tropic bush.

Costa Rica, the most southerly of the five older Republics of Central America, with its total land area of 23,000 square miles, is said to contain 10,000 square miles of forest. On the Atlantic slope, dense forests prevail, but wide savannas are more frequent on the Pacific side. Besides valuable timber and dye-woods, it yields coffee, and 10 million bunches of bananas are exported or have been exported in a single year. This crop is very exacting on the soil, and much of the old banana land should be returned to forest if exhaustion is to be prevented.

Nicaragua, with an area of 51,700 square miles, has a forest area of 25,000 square miles. The history of the country after the severance from Spain is a record of war and dissension, and

although she has made laudable efforts to develop her resources, all too little has been done to perpetuate her forests on
scientific lines.

Salvador, the smallest but most thickly populated of the
Central American Republics, consists of a strip of territory
stretching between Honduras and the Pacific, and is bounded
on the west by Guatemala and on the east by Fonseca Bay,
which separates it from Nicaragua. With a total land area of
13,200 square miles, she only possesses a forest area of 1,200
square miles.

For many years famous for its mahogany, Honduras still
retains virgin forests of considerable size amounting to 6,640
square miles, which have covered the ancient civilization of
the Mayas.

In the uplands of Guatemala are forests of huge pine,
spruce, and oak. Altogether they contain over 100 kinds of
timber trees, including many of the most valuable. To-day
the Mayan peoples retain only legends of their former
greatness.

Cuba is the largest island of the West Indies, being 759 miles
in length from Cape Maysi on the east to Cape Antonio on the
west, with a breadth varying from twenty-seven to ninety
miles and an area of 43,000 square miles, in addition to which
there are 2,000 miles of rocks and islets, including the island
of Pinos, making a total of 45,000 square miles. The forest area
has been estimated at 7,000 square miles, only one per cent of
which is virgin. The high mountains produce woods suitable
for sawing, and have been heavily exploited, along with the
forests of the low mountains, which to-day only provide fire-
wood, charcoal, and other products of small dimension. For
many years the forests of Cuba produced the well-known
swietenia mahogany and other valuable woods. The famous
Mexican cigar-box cedar, *Cedrela Mexicana*, known locally as
cedre, is much in demand, as well as that of three pines known
locally as the male pine tree, *Pinus caribea*, the female pine,
Pinus tropicalis, and the Baracoa pine, *Pinus occidentalis*. No
method of reafforestation has been employed, although some
very small experimental woods have been planted. Selection
is the method employed in using the products of the high

mountains, but complete cutting takes place in the lower mountains. The Cuban forests have suffered ill-effects from the World War II, for the extraction of woods of all kinds has been much increased. Many areas have been entirely devastated and cut for agricultural purposes. The value of the products taken from the forests in 1944 amounted to over £3 million sterling.

Señor Don Julio A. Brodermann, Cuban Consul-General, speaking on the occasion of the second gathering in London held to further a World Charter for Forestry, said:

"On behalf of the Cuban legation in London I had the privilege last time we met to support the movement in favour of the preservation and increase of the forest resources of the world, which means in all countries where lands are available for planting trees, or forests exist.

"I am glad to have the opportunity again to support this movement on behalf of the Cuban Government, who take great interest in this matter. Forests and trees are one of the important sources of wealth of Cuba, and the Government is taking suitable measures to increase and conserve the forest resources of the island.

"This organization, which is doing such excellent work, deserves the support of all governments and of the people everywhere, and I think we can count on their co-operation in preparing a World Charter for Forestry and in carrying out the programme which that Charter will provide. I can assure you of the good will of Cuba in this useful enterprise."

The mountainous country of Haiti is, after Cuba, the largest of the West Indian islands. It has a total area of 11,000 square miles, 5,700 square miles of which is forest.

Santo Domingo is the principal source of lignum vitae, *Guaiacum officinale*, one of the hardest and heaviest woods in the world and one of the most useful of timbers; for a great many purposes it has been found impossible to produce a substitute. The maintenance of a sufficient supply may indeed be said to be a question of world importance. There is nothing equal to it for the making of sheaves for blocks, and when employed in this way it wears well and seems almost imperishable. Perhaps the most important of the many uses to which it is put is the bushing of the stern tubes for propeller shafts in even the largest ships. Owing to the silky nature of the wood and the oil contained in it, acting in conjunction with the water, a natural lubricant is formed. The life of the material when used in this manner is extraordinary and varies from three to seven years, the shortest period being the life of the wood for a fast ship like the *Queen Elizabeth*. It is also used for the packing between saws in machine-saw frames.

Jamaica, or the Land of Springs, the largest and most important of the British West Indies, has little forest left, although the island is transversed from east to west by a range of mountains which are the natural domain of trees and forest. The virgin woods have almost disappeared, yet there are still many valuable trees, such as balata or beef-wood, *Mimusops globosa*, mahogany, logwood, lignum vitae, fustic, ebony, and satin-wood. A far-sighted policy would allow for protective forest belts following the contours of the mountains and providing shelter for the famous Blue Mountain coffee and the many other valuable agricultural crops.

Mexico, with a total area of 760,000 square miles, has about 20 billion cubic feet of pines in her mountain forests at a range of from 7,000 to 10,000 feet, and so far these reserves have not suffered, because the means of extracting timber has been by ox-cart or by mule over poor trails, in a primitive, hand-lumbering way. But those forests will inevitably disappear when modern lumbering tackle is used. In the lowlands, dye-woods and valuable timber abound. Speaking at the World Forestry Charter Luncheon held in London in April, 1945, Señor Dr. Don Alfonso de R. Diaz, the Mexican Ambassador to the Court of St. James, fully endorsed my proposals for the formation of a World Forestry Committee and the preparation of a World Charter for Forestry. He has planted trees, and trees are his hobby. Wandering in many parts of the world, he has devoted time to admiring the most outstanding trees of each country. He recalled in Mexico the famous tree of Tacuba, beneath whose branches the conqueror Hernán Cortés wept; also the tree of Santa Maria del Tule in the State of Oaxaca, with a girth so great that it took thirty men to encircle it; and finally the "Soldado", a millenary tree of the world-unique Chapultepec Forest. In Venezuela he went to see near Macaray the tree called Mato-Palo, beneath whose branches Simon Bolivar and his troops stayed for rest and shade during his wonderful campaigns. In Central America he saw the La Ceiba national tree, the design of which appeared on the coins in that part of the world, with the inscription "Libre crezca Fecundo". In El Salvador he stood awed by the balsamic tree; and in Sweden it was his pleasure to walk round the forests thinking that trees can also be civilized.

"And now I give a call to you," the Ambassador said, "an idea that will surely result in many trees being planted. I propose that we promote the publication of a monumental work dedicated to the tree, which shall contain plates of the most outstanding trees of the world. A Committee might be appointed to study this question and the possibility of its being put into practice under the patronage of the ministers of agriculture of the United Nations."

This present work is a first attempt to create what the Mexican Ambassador had in mind, leading on to the deeper significance which trees hold for mankind.

When the North American Continent was first opened up, trees were felled in large numbers and the virgin soil cleared for exploitation by the new settlers. In many areas this soil was very rich and afforded heavy wheat crops year after year without much care. Many of the early settlers did not trouble at all to replenish or nourish the soil, but moved farther on to fresh virgin soil when the first farm showed signs of depletion. But even farmers trained in England have confessed that they saw the soil simply vanish under their feet in the course of a lifetime of farming in America. It seems hardly credible that a man could learn farming in England, emigrate to America, deplete a number of feet of virgin soil, and return to England to farm again. That would mean destroying soil at the rate of about 1 inch a year, and it takes about 400 years to build up 1 inch of good soil under favourable conditions.

The process is relatively simple. Here was a chance of making money. The timber that was felled brought a good return, which enabled the settler to build his home and gather about him a certain amount of equipment. Good harvests of grain followed year after year, without the necessity of putting much back into the gradually thinning soil. Heat, rain, and wind began to carry away the soil bodily. Deprived of its cover of leaf and blade, the soil was dried up by the summer sun and blown away in clouds of dust. Dust storms in some parts were so bad that they stopped operations in hospitals, because the dust could not be kept out of the operating theatres in the towns. Whole farms were carried away by the wind. Then on sloping ground the water, after rain, cut gullies in the soil or washed it away in sheets, so that the streams and rivers became silted up, and the rivers had to overflow their normal banks. Thus the felling of timber in the uplands affected the surface of the earth as far down as the estuaries or even the sea itself. The 1930s brought the record-breaking floods and dust storms. Practically all crop-growing vitality has been swept from nearly one-seventh of the surface of the United States. Estimates based on the rapid rate of deterioration of the soil during this period were so alarming that it was considered likely that within 100 years the territory of the United States would afford a livelihood for but a few million people along the seaboard, and that the rest of the country would be reduced to irretrievable desert. In any case, it is known that erosion has made its mark upon 1,000 million acres.

In years to come this profligate exploitation of land will no doubt be regarded as sheer madness, and yet to the people who were the actual cause of it—namely, the lumberers, farmers, and ranchers—it did not appear to be robbery and wastage of the national wealth. The fault lies chiefly in our manner of translating wealth into financial figures, and then manipulating the financial figures to estimate the play of social forces. Lumberers and farmers had to pay their way, and the more money they made, the greater was the social esteem in which they were held. Paying your way and making money were perhaps the greatest recognized virtues at the period which brought about the disaster in natural wealth. To the early settlers, it certainly never occurred that the time would come when maltreatment of soil would ever be noticeable in such a vast territory. To them the new land appeared utterly

inexhaustible. But their example, followed by millions of suc-
cessors, told a different story: the appalling one which is now
familiar to us all.

The record-breaking floods and widespread dust storms of
the 1930's dramatized the power of soil erosion, deepened
economic depression, and intensified its effects upon the
people. On all sides it became abundantly clear that conservation of the soil was a national necessity of the very highest
order.

A nation-wide soil-erosion control was launched for the first
time in United States history and pushed forward along
several fronts. Government technicians and Civilian Conservation Corps enrollees went into erosion-problem areas and
helped farmers lay down defences against rain and wind.
Benefit payments were made available to all land-operators
who adopted specified soil-saving practices. State laws were
passed giving farmers the power to form local co-operative
societies for soil and water conservation.

In this many-sided movement, the Soil Conservation Service
has played and is playing a major role. Through a programme
of research and farmland demonstrations, the Service has developed and improved practical measures of erosion control.
The specific land treatments used and recommended by the
Service vary from one valley to the next, from farm to farm,
and even from field to field. Before any work is done, each farm
or ranch is analysed both as a piece of land and as a business
enterprise.

In making the physical analysis, fieldmen of the Soil Conservation Service carefully note the lie of the land, the qualities
of the soil, and the erosion hazards on every acre. As accurately
as possible, they determine which lands can be cultivated
under rotation practices without excessive soil loss, which lands
need the protection afforded by special crop arrangements or
special tillage practices, and which ones require a permanent
safeguarding cover of trees or grass.

The next step in soil conservation is to work out a new farm
layout based on the survey information. Steep or unproductive
croplands, for example, may be earmarked for permanent
cover of grass or trees; farm forests may be planned where grass

is not paying, or where it is failing to hold the soil; gullied areas may be turned into grass-covered waterways or small-scale sanctuaries for animals and birds. The end in view is a new arrangement of fields, pastures, meadows, and woods that guards the soil and fits the land as Nature made it.

In many cases, this new layout may not entirely fit the farmer's pocket-book. It may call for more hay crops than he actually needs, and not enough cotton or corn; it may involve other changes that he simply cannot afford to make. If so, it is not a good layout in the final sense of the word, and it must be adjusted to family needs and market opportunities. Purely from the conservation standpoint, however, the layout based on physical land analysis is ideal. The closer the farmer can approach it and still make a living, the more stable and productive his land will be over the long run of years.

Drawing up a satisfactory land use layout is only half the job of planning for erosion control on the farm. Each parcel of land, even under the new use, generally needs some special practices or treatments for adequate soil protection. Croplands are nearly always farmed in rotation, usually on the level, and sometimes in strips; terraces are frequently built for added protection. Pastures are limed, fertilized, and grazed with caution to improve the growth of soil-guarding grass. Woodlands are fenced to keep out livestock, protected from fire, and managed according to scientific principles of forestry. These are only a few of the dozens of erosion-control practices that may be called into play. The new layout, *plus* the practices, makes up a complete farm plan for soil and water conservation. Under such a plan, soil conservation is not just an incidental farming activity; it becomes part and parcel of the whole business of making a living from the land.

Trees are one of Nature's most efficient weapons of soil defence. Conservation farmers use them to tie down steep hillsides, to check the growth of big gullies, to stabilize unsteady stream banks, and to screen off cultivated fields from harmful winds. At the same time trees also help to keep money in the family pocket-book, for they provide fuel for the home, posts for fences, timber for repairing barns and sheds, and saw-logs for sale in the nearby markets. The ultimate goal of the Soil

Conservation Service is a comprehensive inventory of the
country's soil potentialities, an inventory that will aid farmers
and farmer groups as well as local, state, and federal agencies
in charting a safe and intelligent course for American
agriculture.

It is a tragedy that in a country of 3,026,800 square miles
there remains only an area of 284,000 square miles of exploit-
able forest. The people of the United States are eating into
their forest capital at four and a half times the rate of the
annual wood increment. They have cut seven-eighths of their
virgin forests. Against that they have a secondary crop coming
on in many parts where it was cut, but there have been colossal
fires which have taken their toll. For many years the U.S.A.
has had to resort to Canada for supplies of timber for pulp
wood. Newsprint only represents about thirteen per cent of the
total amount of woodpulp used; thirty per cent, for instance,
is used as kraft or wrapping paper, and almost every day finds
a new use for forest products in one form or another.

The development of the Dominion of Canada has been made
possible by its extensive waterways and railway systems, and,
conversely, the natural resources of Canada have made their
development possible. The boasted inexhaustibility of Canada's
forests is an expression which should be used guardedly.
Canada, like other countries rich in forest resources, has been
extravagant and careless, though there are many hopeful
signs that progressive forest protection measures in their
broadest sense have advanced from theory to practice. There
is still, however, a long, hard road ahead. Forest protection in
all its branches—against fire, disease, insects—is greater to-day
than ever before. As Canada matures, the importance of
scientific conservation and utilization is assuming its rightful
place in the Dominion's economy and progress. The matter
must not be brought to public attention only: it must be kept
alive and advanced by sound legislation and education. Forest
conservation is primarily education. Much may be learned
from the experience of others, but our own experiences are,
and will be, our best teacher. The law of itself does not put out
forest fires. The only policeman worth while in our woods is
the man who polices himself.

Canada, together with Newfoundland and Labrador, has a total area of 3,629,250 square miles, of which 1,290,960 square miles are forest, but only 810,000 square miles are classed as being of productive quality.

In eastern Canada the principal softwood species are spruces: red, white, and jackpine; balsam fir, hemlock, and cedar. The most important hardwoods are maple, birch, and poplar. On the west coast, the chief species are Douglas fir, western hemlock, and western red cedar, and these are accompanied by smaller quantities of pine, Sitka spruce, and true fir. In general, natural regeneration is relied upon throughout the forests, but about 20,000 acres have been planted annually. The total area of forests controlled by the Crown is 1,190,785 square miles, including both productive and unproductive forest areas. More than nine-tenths of all the forests in Canada belong to the public, and are known as Crown forests. They are managed by governments on behalf of the people. Forests in the North-west and Yukon Territories, and those in National Parks and Forest Experiment Stations, are controlled by the Federal Government, but all other Crown forests are administered by the governments of the provinces in which they stand. Several provinces, notably Quebec, Ontario, and British Columbia, maintain large forest nurseries where planting stock is grown both for forest plantings and for the supply of farmers. Permanent nursery stations are maintained. Permanent staffs are small, but considerable local employment is provided during the transplanting seasons. The output of these stations runs into millions of small trees annually.

Accessible, merchantable saw-timber is estimated at 60 billion cubic feet, and pulp-wood at 50 billions. The forests are being exploited two and a half times as fast as the wood increment. Canada has about enough to last twenty-five years at the present rate of cutting or destruction. She is using about three-fifths of the lumber she produces, and as her population grows her timber requirements may be expected to increase also. Dominion foresters are expressing grave concern over the situation. Fortunately, sweeping changes in forestry laws are now being made. In this matter, the move is coming from the far west, and, when it meets again in the near future, the Provincial Legislature will hear proposals for sweeping changes in statutes relating to British Columbia's leading source of revenue, its vast forest industry. The Government, which last spring began a step-by-step implementation of the Sloan Commission's recommendations, by appropriating an extra $1,000,000 for forest fire protection, will go much farther in the next phase of its forest plan, bringing down legislation that is likely to rate as the most important and far-reaching of the session's work.

With strong emphasis on reafforestation, it is believed the new measures to be introduced will be directed towards placing the entire industry on a sustained yield basis—strongly advocated by Chief Justice Gordon Sloan.

The exact nature of the Government's proposals has not been disclosed, but it is understood that the new policy will embrace provisions to ensure reafforestation of logged-off lands, regulation of logging methods to prevent destructive exploitation, and revision of taxation and tenure system, to encourage private forestry and remove causes compelling liquidation.

Forest Department Officials already are working on the first draft of the proposed legislation, closely following the recommendations of Chief Justice Sloan, who, in his report as Royal Commissioner, said:

". . . The present policy of unmanaged liquidation of our forest wealth must give way to the important concept of a planned forest policy designed to maintain our forests upon the principle of sustained yield production. Our forest land must be regarded as a source of renewable crops, and not as a mine to be exploited and abandoned."

The Canadian National railway system, with its 22,000 miles of active trackage, some 1,840 miles of which are in the U.S.A. and the balance in Canada, needs some 60 million railway cross-ties or sleepers to carry the steel rails. The average yearly purchase of cross-ties is about 8 million. About ninety-three per cent of these are soft woods, seven per cent hard woods. Although fires caused by locomotives have shown a marked decrease, due largely to mechanical improvements and the use of better grade coal, they still levy their toll on the forests. The Canadian National railways maintain twenty-five fire fighting tank cars, varying in capacity from 3,000 to 13,000 gallons, equipped with steam and petrol power pumps. These are stationed at strategic points along the railway, and are kept in readiness during the fire season. Some 14,000 miles of territory are classified as forested, and on this mileage special patrol or attention is provided. But railway engines are not the only cause of forest fires, which annually devastate hundreds of thousands of acres. The careless tourist is responsible for many an outbreak. One tree will make a million matches, but one match, carelessly thrown away, may destroy a million trees.

Farm woodlots are making a valuable contribution towards the forest resources and are already contributing a large proportion of wood for all purposes. They are privately owned, and well-managed farm plantations are increasing the prosperity of the agricultural communities. Disease control is carried on in close collaboration with the Department of Agriculture, which maintains two tree-planting stations at Indian Head and Sutherland, Saskatchewan. These stations provide planting stock, for the establishment of wind-breaks and shelter-belts, to farmers in the three prairie provinces.

Crossing the expanse of the Atlantic Ocean, our minds revert to the cataclysmic disaster that overtook the one time vast continent of Atlantis, the great expanse of land which stretched over the site of the present ocean. Many writers concede that the eastern extremity of this submerged continent incorporated what is now the western fringe of Europe, and that the step up to this area was Ireland, the western part of the British Isles, the Channel Islands, that part of France known as Armorica or Brittany, as well as Spain and Portugal; that it extended further south and included part of Western Africa, the Azores, Madeira, the Canaries, Tristan da Cunha, Ascension and St. Paul being the outstanding peaks. These authorities seem to agree that the final subsidence of this continent took place about 9560 years B.C. The Troano MS. in the museum at Madrid confirms this date, and agrees with the time given by Plato in his *Critias* and the *Timaeus*.

Students of the mystery of Atlantis tell us that the tragedy and disaster of that continent came by reason of the desire of the later Atlanteans to create for baser ends; instead of exercising true dominion over the elements, they sought to prostitute their powers and dissipate them in defiance of the Divine law of the Universe.

I have flown over many parts of the world and studied the problem of erosion in many countries, and have slept on the sand in deserts, where the ever-moving particles have banked up around me during the night; I have witnessed the incursions made by the sea upon many a coast-line, and the power of rivers in flood, bearing away millions of tons of earth and stone, and have also stood on the top of the Grand Canyon, gazing across an abyss of fifteen miles, seeing how the Colorado River has been cutting away ever deeper and deeper into the bowels of the earth. Having seen the power of wind and water erosion, with such evidence in my mind, I cannot resist the belief that the prime cause of the Atlantian disaster was deforestation and erosion.

Atlantis went down because the people had denatured it and had become too luxurious in their mode of living. The best of the stock, reading the signs of pending disaster, migrated, and many of them became hill farmers in Britain, which was then on the fringe of their Empire. They have left behind them monumental works which may have been temples or observatories or even power stations. The earthworks of Maiden Castle, Abbotsbury Castle, and thirty-eight more ringed hills of Wessex may possibly have been the great ritualistic assembly places of the people of those distant days.

Finally, the subsidence of Atlantis took place, with those that remained living there, and the sea covered the tired land to give it a rest from human molestation. There have been successive invasions of the British forests which have sheltered those unconquerable spirits who would not be divorced from nature or bow to passing fashions. The Romans did not conquer Britons by force of arms, for the forests protected them; it was not until the country was bribed to export wheat to feed the people of Rome that the forests were seriously invaded and destroyed to provide the land to grow wheat to make money.

In spite of the Romans, the core of England remained primeval forest.

Down through the ages, the forests of these favoured islands have provided food and shelter. Despite the efforts of all her enemies to mar and scar the face of this green and pleasant land, the trees still function, though only as scattered woodlands, too often neglected. Even when destroyed, trees leave their traces on the face of the country, truthfully recording aggression by water, ice, or man. Their influence, too, remains and inspirits the very being of the people.

But there has been a growing demand for luxury, tending to turn men from a natural life and soften them in the process. A mere whim followed by a king or a queen is copied by the courtiers and is handed down through the various strata until the mass of people claim it as their right. The pyramid becomes inverted and economic stability is threatened. The story of Britain is that of forest destruction. A few ancient yews still remain as witnesses of the last 2,000 years of English life. There are a few oaks, too, *Quercus robur*, signs of original forest trees which would form an interesting biological study. The few surviving giants of the forest are decrepit with age. The ravages of man have left but a few survivors to deplore the process of urbanization and the reduction of the economic forest area to but three per cent of the total area of the land. The First World War was the means of reducing Britain's forest by 800,000 acres, and the Second World War cost 1 million acres. Land alienated to-day by the War Office for training purposes amounts to another two million acres of ground. Besides the land sterilized by the War Department, there are at least seven and a half million idle acres below the standard of agriculture which might well be dedicated to the growing of trees. Much of this land consists of steep hillsides which urgently need forest covering, and which in the early days of colonization were covered with virgin growth. Most of our forests have vanished, and to-day Great Britain, with a land area of 80,000 square miles, has a total forest covering of less than one-sixteenth, while only half of this can be regarded as forest of economic value. English improvidence may be compared with that of Spain and Italy in past centuries, and is only equalled by that of the U.S.A. and Australia to-day. In the Ice Age the forests of Britain were forced to retreat, but they were not vanquished. Modern urbanization is a greater menace than the glaciers of old.

P

Chapter Twenty-one

FOR THE HEALING OF THE NATIONS

. . . And the leaves of the tree were for the healing of the nations.

Rev. 22: 2.

THE HEALTH AND THE ECONOMIC SECURITY OF THE HUMAN race depend on how well the forests of the world are managed. All the countries of the world are suffering the penalty resulting from man's neglect to plant where he has reaped. He has destroyed the gifts of a generous Creator without realizing that they were a trust to be handed on to future generations. The earth's green covering is Nature's capital, and, if man exacts more than the interest or annual increment, he is endangering the source of wealth and the very means of his existence on the planet.

The forest is the mother of the rivers and one of Nature's most important means of regulating and maintaining the flow and quality of water. How the forests are managed decides whether the rain and snow they receive will be a blessing or catastrophe. Water is the priceless resource on which all growing things depend. It is the life-blood of the earth. Where there are ample supplies of good water, vigorous nations can flourish, farms thrive, and cities prosper. When the supply of water fails, farms are abandoned, communities are impoverished, and cities and cultures die, leaving crumbling ruins to mark their transient glory.

History has shown that Nature exacts payment for her abuse, and disaster follows when man breaks the divine law of the universe. Earth is a sentient being and feels the behaviour of the sons of men, whom she has nurtured upon her breast. Is it to be wondered that she is wilting under severe maltreatment? Man, in his dire folly, has removed vast areas of virgin forest, and now the end of earth's sylvan wealth is in sight.

There is no time to be lost if man is to be saved from bringing disaster on this planet and himself. The tragedies and disasters that overtook the dwellers on the continents of Atlantis and Mu are a solemn warning of what may await a civilization which disregards natural laws.

Water is the source of life to a man dying of thirst or a farm needing irrigation, but it can also be a deadly enemy to all life when uncontrolled by the essential forest covering. Urban water-users and valley-dwellers, though remote from the watershed forests, are bound to suffer the consequences of damaged uplands. All people should demand that reasonable tree cover be maintained, so that erosion and rapid run-off be prevented; otherwise their health and well-being are imperilled. Every man, woman, and child is really under duress not to waste water or use it without thought for Nature's own needs. As people learn more about the essential tree cover and appreciate the increasing value of forests for watershed protection, they will see to it that the forests are not maltreated. Forest fires, which are largely the result of carelessness or thoughtlessness, continue to do great damage, threatening to deplete and reduce the tree cover to a point at which it cannot adequately serve its function. By the prevention of forest fires, enormous annual losses to every interest and section of the community may be minimized. There should be adequate conservation laws in every country, and governments should purchase suitable watershed, cut-over, idle, and semi-arid lands for reafforestation under scientific forestry supervision. All means possible should be employed to encourage the planting of trees and the creation of forests to provide sufficient cover, so that an approximation to the natural circulation of water may be restored.

We believe that the great task of conserving and replenishing the forests of the world and reclaiming the deserts and waste places by tree planting requires the concerted action of every country, and at the same time provides a common meeting ground for all men. We believe that in order to save humanity we must save men, and in order to save the forests we must save the trees. To live our bodily life on this earth we must get food, clothes, and shelter. To do this we must take care of the earth beneath our feet and especially not meddle wantonly with the natural circulation of water, which meddling has been the cause of great loss of soil all over the globe. We must rightly return to the earth the waste of whatever we take from it. In saving the forests of the world, we accomplish all these ends. But as we look out on the world to-day we see that monster cities are tapping wider areas, and the water table is sinking in all areas of civilization. A halt must be called; otherwise the means of life will vanish. It is not our aim to clothe the surface of the earth with an unbroken forest cover, but rather to see to it that every city has its catchment area and every farm and hamlet its protecting trees. We visualize valley settlement as the cradle of sound culture. Food is the first necessity of a healthy, industrious and happy life. It will be a whole life, balanced in every respect, in which well-being is not necessarily the result of financial success, but the outcome of work well done without thought of personal gain; each and all working together for the good of the whole. The accomplishment of this purpose will assure not only the perpetuation of the forests through intelligent use, and the preservation of real wealth in growing trees and forests, but the regeneration of the very spirit of man, for in this life he may find the highest and the best.

World afforestation is necessary because it is the most constructive and peaceable enterprise in which the nations could co-operate. It would check, stop, and reverse the advance of the deserts upon the good lands of the globe, and thus relieve the growing shortage of foods. If food sources are allowed to become more restricted than they are at present, the tendency to grab unlawfully for them will increase intolerably, thus making for war with its large-scale destruction; whereas, if genuine co-operation can be rallied internationally for the purpose of preserving and increasing the primary producing areas of the land surface, the tendency will be towards peace and future prosperity.

With the object of furthering such international co-operation, the Society of the Men of the Trees has sponsored gatherings in London for representatives of the Diplomatic Corps. Those attending included officials from twenty-four countries, and the resolution placed before the last gathering by the Chairman, the Right Honourable Lord Sempill, was passed unanimously for transmission to the United Nations Organization:

"That, realizing in face of the present world famine the dependence of Man on trees and forests, and, seeing the forests disappearing and the deserts encroaching on the remaining food sources at a rate of up to thirty miles per year on 1,000-mile fronts in three continents, this gathering of national representatives of twenty-four countries request the aid of U.N.O. in the preparation of a WORLD CHARTER FOR FORESTRY."

The United Nations Organization has taken the matter up in response to the World Forestry Committee's resolution, and its investigating section accepted from us a few directions for eventual recommendation to all member nations of U.N.O. We are well aware that it may be a long way from this stage of investigation to the time when reafforestation becomes a first priority in world undertakings. But the start we have made is encouraging, and we shall no doubt advance rapidly because we have Nature herself to back us. The nations of the world and not merely their experts and political leaders are gradually waking to the consciousness that the shortage of food and other primary products may not cure itself with inertia and time. We say *may* not, because it is possible that, by removing human interference and taking the job on herself, Nature could restore the cover of the earth with inertia and time. This is a very important point, as it is suggested by some experts that out-worked territories should be sealed off and left to the healing work of Nature, instead of being replanted with trees, as we urge. But if the cure is left to Nature, it is most likely that the disturbers—that is to say, we human beings—may be thinned out very thoroughly to facilitate the cure of earth's distress. The means of thinning us out is temptingly handy in present political friction and scientific instruments of modern warfare.

We have already advanced to U.N.O. the suggestion that the minimum of safety in tree cover is ten per cent of the habitable land area. Therefore, the first step we urge towards the restoration of balance is tree-planting up to ten per cent of every catchment area of every state subscribing to the policy of world afforestation.

The next step we advocate is the formation of a faculty or

university of land reclamation, a world centre where this all-important problem may be studied and at the same time put into practice. Such a body might be founded in the foothills of the Atlas Mountains of North Africa, surrounded by land which in course of time has been exploited and become unproductive. This centre would welcome research students and members of forestry and farming faculties elected from universities and schools from every nation. It might be called the University of Atlas, for in that classic name are implications of its world-wide nature. It might become not only a repository for the latest and best scientific information in all matters relating to land reclamation and afforestation, but demonstrate by practical example how best to reclaim waste lands and deserts. This university should be endowed by all nations, and adequate resources should be placed at its disposal for carrying into effect a large-scale reclamation programme which would provide work for 1,000 years. Funds commensurate with those at present devoted to armaments should be forthcoming for the gigantic task of reclaiming the waste places of the earth.

As a practical demonstration of what can be done, water might be taken from the Gulf of Gabes and, sweetened by fourteen miles of proper conduits, used to flood an area of three hundred square miles of desert below sea level. This would provide an inland sea and transport for the flourishing areas which would spring up in its neighbourhood as a result of bio-technical methods. The rivers flowing south and north from the Atlas, Aures, and Tebessa Mountains might be manipulated to provide power and fertility. This centre would become a starting point for a wider reclamation programme, which would in time embrace the whole of the Sahara and the Libyan Deserts.

We advocate that all standing armies everywhere be used for the work of essential reafforestation, in the first instance, in the countries to which they belong, and that each country, as it is able to spare men, shall provide expeditionary forces to co-operate in the greater tasks of land reclamation in the Sahara and other deserts. Armies are risky factors in countries where the people cannot be fed, and they will not provide security unless essential food is forthcoming generally. I am confident that all this can be done. The world is technically so far advanced that it is not in a position to stand the privation of descent into chaos and extinction. Under the palpable danger of approaching ruin, it is possible for the best and highest to exercise their authority and turn man from racial suicide back to the light of reasonable preservation.

Archæologists have given us the story of the rise and fall of nations. Each in turn reached its peak of prosperity, then vanished. We have learned that civilization is an intermittent and recurrent phenomenon, that it sprouts and flourishes, decays and dies. Each successive civilization had its great year, followed by impotence. Each in turn arrived at the cross-roads of time, where it was confronted with the necessity of deciding which way to turn.

The red lights are against us in our reckless career. To continue to rape the earth and fight for dwindling supplies of food and timber, spells destruction. The murky rivers, charged with earth from many a mountainside, tell their story and are danger signals. Following upon forest destruction, overstocking, and exhaustive cultivation, erosion is taking place over vast tracts of the earth's surface. Let us remember that the empires of Babylon, Syria, Persia, and Carthage were destroyed by the advance of floods and deserts caused by the increasing clearing of forests for farmland. Can the present reckless race to destruction be checked? Will man agree to conserve and replenish the earth and stem the march of the oncoming deserts? It is not merely a national question, but a world undertaking, in which every nation and every member of the human race must take his share.

The Second World War cost the nations much material. A further war might cost double the amount and reduce us to dire distress. If we spent as generously on land reclamation and reafforestation, we should immediately remove the spectre of world war, safeguard the forests, and ensure the prosperous well-being of mankind for generations to come.

The world task which I have attempted to outline calls for authoritative action from the highest and best, and the country that provides the lead in this fateful hour will rise above political and national rivalries and have the support of Heaven and earth. "For the earth is the Lord's and the fulness thereof." Such work, if done in the spirit of worship, will count as worship. By saving the forests and maintaining the tree cover the sudden decline to which civilizations are prone will be avoided.

Such a lead will command the support of the choice spirits in all lands. In times past it has been said that it is the duty of a man to be prepared to die for his country; to-day it is the duty of every thinking being to live, and to serve not only his own day and generation, but also generations unborn by helping to restore and maintain the green glory of the forests of the earth.

INDEX